The
Colourful World
of Birds

The Colourful World of Birds

Euan Dunn

Sundial

Contents

First published 1976 by
Sundial Books Limited
59 Grosvenor Street
London W1

© 1976 Hennerwood Publications Limited

ISBN 0 904230 16 3

Printed in Great Britain by
Jarrold & Sons Limited

Flight

Around 200 million years ago, the land was dominated by the reptiles we call dinosaurs and some of the small terrestrial forms of these are believed to have been the earliest ancestors of birds. The first evidence of this connection emerged from the exciting discovery in 1861 of a strange fossil in Bavaria. This celebrated animal, named *Archaeopteryx*, was about crow size and was part reptile, part bird. It bore undeniable reptilian characteristics—toothed jaws and a bony tail—but it was covered with feathers indistinguishable from those of modern flying birds. The creature was certainly not capable of active flight, and is thought to have lived in the tree canopy, where at best it would have made faltering glides to lower branches or to the ground, most likely to catch insects in its snapping jaws. Once grounded, it could use the claws on its rudimentary wings to clamber back up to the tree tops. It is clear then that *Archaeopteryx* was only a small step away from a true flying bird.

For a time, this knowledge gave rise to considerable controversy over the origin of the flightless birds alive today. These, like the Ostrich and Emu, are significantly lacking in the deep breast-bone, or keel, which is the anchorage for the powerful wing muscles of birds that fly. Could this mean that the flightless birds are even nearer to the original reptilian line than was *Archaeopteryx*? Closer scrutiny of the skeletons of flightless birds shows that this is not so, that they are in fact merely degenerate flying forms. So there must have been a time when all birds were capable of flight and some, through an evolutionary change, subsequently became flightless.

Before we explore the world of flying birds, it is worth examining this select band of somewhat bizarre flightless birds. The first thing we notice about them is that they are mostly very large and bulky, as indeed only flightless birds could be. Some of the largest are now extinct, which is not surprising since they would have been easy prey to early hunting man. Notable amongst these are the Elephant Birds of Mada-

gascar, now known only from fossil remains. From reconstructions, it has been estimated that the biggest of them stood ten feet (3.1 metres) tall and weighed 1000 pounds. They were birds of open country where their massive long legs were ideally suited to rapid travel. A number of their enormous eggs have also been found; these had a liquid content of two gallons (about nine litres) which gives them the distinction of being the largest known single cells in the animal kingdom. Little wonder that in native legend the birds which laid such eggs were thought capable of carrying off an elephant, and thus acquired their popular name.

The Moas in New Zealand had similar characteristics. Their sizes varied, from the smallest around three feet (one metre) high to the largest which equalled the Elephant Bird in height. Sadly, the Moas became extinct in quite recent times through over hunting by the Maoris. It is probable that the last sighting of a small species was made in the late nineteenth century, although some believe that a few individuals may

BELOW A male Ostrich *(Struthio camelus)*, the largest living bird, with its family of chicks. Though flightless, Ostriches can out-run most predators.

RIGHT A pair of Fulmars *(Fulmarus glacialis)*, experts at using updraughts at cliffs to stay airborne with the minimum of effort.

6

yet survive in remote parts of the montane forests.

Despite this gloomy record of extinction, a number of spectacular flightless birds still exist, and include our largest living birds. The modern equivalents of the Elephant Birds and Moas are fortunately widely distributed – the Ostriches of Africa, the Emus of Australia, the Cassowaries of New Guinea, and the Rheas of South America. Like their near ancestors, they are all large, long-legged birds, equipped for fast running. All have vestigial wings, which indicate that they have long since lost the power of flight. Some, like the Cassowary, have sought refuge from hunters by invading dense forest, where their secretive habits make them more often heard than seen.

The diminutive Kiwi, about the size of a domestic fowl, has further enhanced its survival by assuming a nocturnal existence. It inhabits the thick New Zealand bush where even its thin reedy voice rarely betrays its whereabouts. Apart from man, New Zealand has no

native predators of birds, which explains why so many flightless forms have managed to survive. A much rarer native of that country, the Kakapo or Owl Parrot, is scarcely better endowed with flying powers than was *Archaeopteryx*. Like the Kiwi it is active only at night, and spends most of its time on the ground or clambering up trees, from where it can only manage gliding flights on its weak wings.

Most of the flightless species described so far belong to the group we call Ratites—birds which no longer use their wings as a means of propulsion—but these are not the only birds that have dispensed with flight. The penguins represent the other major line: they have evolved wings that are ideal for 'flying' in water. The eighteen species are well distributed, and without exception are confined to the southern hemisphere, where they must have originated. In place of the loose feathers characteristic of flying birds, they have evolved a plumage of dense, scale-like feathers. Apart from making them superbly streamlined for swimming underwater, this thick coat also insulates penguins against the sub-zero temperatures that many of them experience in their Antarctic home. The largest and best-known inhabitants of this inhospitable environment are the Emperor Penguins, which breed in the depth of the Antarctic winter. Their wings have become modified into strong narrow flippers with which they propel themselves underwater, often at great speed, steering with the aid of their webbed feet and rudder-like tail.

The Great Auk evolved in the same way as the penguins, but other auks—like the Razorbill, Puffin and Guillemot—have evolved a compromise, wings that can be used for propulsion both in the air and under water, so that the birds are almost equally good at coping with either medium.

Throughout evolution, therefore, a few species of flightless birds have successfully competed with mammals on the ground and beneath the seas, and have become well estab-

ABOVE LEFT Kiwi *(Apteryx australis)* of New Zealand.

BELOW LEFT Cassowary *(Casuarius casuarius)*.

ABOVE Kakapo or Owl Parrot *(Strigops habroptilus)*.

BELOW King Penguin *(Aptenodytes patagonica)*.

ABOVE RIGHT A White Stork *(Ciconia ciconia)* about to alight at its nest. The wings are beating forwards, their tips spread to maintain lift, and the legs flexed to absorb the impact.

BELOW RIGHT Hovering enables this Sooty Tern *(Sterna fuscata)* to search for prey in the sea below, and poises it for the capture attempt.

BELOW The airstream deflected upwards by a mountainside provides ideal soaring conditions for the Griffon Vulture *(Gyps fulvus).*

lished. But the great majority of birds have perfected flight, a skill mastered only by bats amongst mammals. It is not difficult to see the advantages that flight gives to birds, for it greatly increases their chances of survival. Flight allows birds to disperse widely in search of food, often to the extent of migrating rapidly over long distances, and also gives easy escape from predators and other dangers.

Birds have been highly efficient in adapting to this flying role, combining the necessity of lightness and streamlining with strength and power. Although man has also made great strides with his flying machines, none of them surpasses any single flying bird in flexibility of shape and subtlety of movement. Nonetheless, no one bird is equally adept at all techniques of flight, and the great diversity of size and shape found amongst birds arises largely from specialization in a particular mode of flying. This in turn is dictated by the sort of environment in which it lives, and especially by its methods of hunting and feeding.

Of the various kinds of flight, the simplest is undoubtedly gliding, since it involves the least expenditure of energy on the bird's part. Before it can glide, however, a bird needs to gain height, so that even the most expert gliders sometimes have to resort to flapping flight to get aloft. Moreover, gliding requires a surprising degree of exertion. Even to keep the wings outstretched, the bird constantly has to resist the tendency of air pressure to thrust its wings upwards. Moreover, the air is a deceptively uniform environment to us, but to a bird it

represents a turbulent maze of ever-changing updraughts, downdraughts, and eddies. Thus the gliding bird is continuously having to adjust the trim of its wings and tail to compensate for these forces, and its evident control merely emphasizes how instinctively the correct adjustments are made.

The distinguishing feature of most birds that glide a great deal is the great length and breadth of their wings. The reason for this is quite simple. In order to stay airborne with the minimum of effort, a bird needs to get as much 'lift' as possible, and one way of achieving this is to increase its wing area. Eagles, with wings characteristic of this type, spend much of their time gliding in the air, in an apparently aimless fashion. All the time, however, the bird is carefully scanning the terrain below for the least sign of movement that might pinpoint its prey. Storks are equally skilful at wheeling for hours on end on outstretched wings, while pelicans, which are heavy birds for their size, often save energy by intermittent spells of gliding. Game birds also utilize gliding flight, though it is of a different type, and over much shorter distances than that of birds of prey. A pheasant or partridge flushed from cover will bolt into the air on its broad, blunt wings, and glide some distance to safety, interrupting its passive flight with only a few rapid wingbeats if it needs to travel further.

Gliding usually involves some loss of height, but under certain conditions this technique allows birds not only to maintain their altitude, but even to increase it. In order to soar in this

way, the bird still uses little energy of its own, so it must harness other forces. The necessary uplift is supplied in a variety of ways, and birds have been quick to exploit all of them to save energy. Some birds make use of the airstreams deflected upwards by major obstacles such as cliffs and mountainsides. Thus on windy days, gulls and fulmars can often be seen suspended on outspread wings above sea cliffs, leisurely side-slipping when they detect a subtle shift of the air that supports them. Some birds adopt this strategy on migration, following a route of mountain ridges where they can depend on upcurrents to help them.

In some areas where the sun rapidly heats the ground, the warmth is transferred to the air which then rises in columns known as thermals. Although we mainly associate thermals with the tropics, they may develop anywhere on land on a sunny day, in woodland clearings, above fields, and even over towns. As a result, many different birds have learned to detect these updraughts and exploit them. Probably the best exponents of this skill are the African vultures, which spiral slowly to the top of one thermal and then glide down to begin ascending on another. In this way they cover great distances over the plains, effortlessly searching the ground below for the carrion that forms the bulk of their diet.

Thermals of this kind only develop over dry land, so many gliding birds are loathe to cross wide tracts of water where this source of lift is unavailable. For this reason, gliding birds on migration stick to land routes as far as possible, even to the extent of hugging narrow peninsulas. In Europe, the White Stork, the Crane and almost all the large birds of prey that winter in Africa, skirt the Black Sea and Mediterranean by crossing at their narrowest points.

Nevertheless, using a completely different set of principles, the albatrosses, large petrels, and shearwaters have learned to soar on the high winds that scour the ocean surface. As we have seen, broad wings are specially designed for gentle and steady updraughts, and strong

gusts would easily unbalance them. Instead of these, the ocean soarers are equipped with narrow, cleaving wings which allow for sensitive control in turbulent conditions. For the same reason, the wing needs to be very rigid over its entire length, which is all the more remarkable when we consider the enormous wingspans involved, up to eleven feet (3.4 metres) in the case of the Wandering Albatross. The albatrosses are undoubtedly among the most masterful of all flying birds. Outside the breeding season, they spend all their time at sea, soaring on motionless, outstretched wings, and only occasionally alighting on the water to feed.

Their soaring flight is not straight, but follows a regular zig-zag path. Picking up speed on the high tailwinds 50–100 feet (16–33 metres) above the waves, the bird swoops down to the surface. Here the wind velocity is reduced by friction, and the bird then turns to soar into the headwind, gaining height for its next burst of acceleration. In this fashion, such birds may cover vast distances, and some albatrosses circumnavigate the globe several times in the space of a lifetime.

Many of the largest species, however, range only within the belt of the southern oceans, aptly known as The Roaring Forties for its almost permanent gale-force winds. So dependent is their sort of soaring on the strength and regularity of these gales, that to wander into less windy latitudes would be to risk getting becalmed. A few albatrosses have broken through the windless tropical belt known as The Doldrums to reach the northern hemisphere, but we can only assume that they did so in the wake of an exceptional storm, or were carried on board ship.

Soaring flight of any description is only practicable for relatively large birds, and while smaller birds can glide, they cannot soar with any degree of control. All small birds must generate their own motive power, and they achieve this by strenuously beating their wings. The motion of the wings is complex, but basically it is the angle of the wing which produces both the lift and the all-important forward thrust needed to propel the bird.

The simplest form of flapping flight is seen during take-off. For heavy birds tremendous lift is needed to get them airborne, and vigorous flapping alone is sometimes insufficient to achieve this. Such birds, like aircraft, need an assisted take-off. Thus swans gain the necessary acceleration by making a runway of the water surface, simultaneously running along it and beating their wings until they generate enough

lift to get airborne. Flamingos take off in a similar fashion from their shallow lagoon feeding grounds. If these birds were any heavier, no amount of exertion would get them off the ground, and in general around 40 pounds (eighteen kilograms) is thought to be the upper weight limit for flying birds.

Birds smaller than swans can usually take off from a standing start, without resorting to any leg-power beyond a powerful spring. At the same time, they angle the body upwards and beat their wings with great force. Some birds, however, have legs that are too short and weak to assist take-off in this way, and these need to adopt a different strategy. The best examples are the swifts, which spend more time in the air than any other bird, and excel in flying skill. However, they have such weak legs that take-off from flat ground is extremely difficult for them. They are further handicapped by having long sickle-shaped wings which are ideal for fast, manoeuvrable flight, but are ill-designed for mustering the initial lift crucial to take-off. For these reasons, swifts never alight on the ground if they can help it, and instead land on vertical walls and cliffs from where they can launch off by swooping vertically downwards.

After take-off, flapping assumes a more leisurely pace, the wing rowing the bird through the air, like a flexible oar. All of the propulsive force is produced on the powerful downstroke, and the upstroke, effected by a kind of rope-and-pulley system, is usually unproductive. As soon as the bird begins to lose

ABOVE RIGHT The long, tapering wings of the Light-mantled Albatross *(Phoebetria palpebrata)* adapt it for soaring.

RIGHT A flock of Mute Swans *(Cygnus olor)* gains momentum for take-off by running along the water surface.

height, therefore, it compensates with a powerful downbeat of its wings. Many small birds, like finches and wagtails, save energy by alternating bursts of vigorous flapping with spells of free fall, when the wings may almost be closed altogether. This produces a very characteristic undulating flight, which is particularly noticeable in woodpeckers.

Another energy-saving device, which has only recently been understood, is the formation-flying of birds which regularly undertake strenuous, long-distance journeys. Anyone fortunate enough to live near a migration route of geese, swans, or cranes, will be familiar with their V-formations as they pass overhead, the two tight-knit lines trailing behind a leading bird. The individual birds are even more co-ordinated than is apparent, since their wing-beats are highly synchronized. The currently held explanation for this behaviour is that a beating wing produces a small upcurrent at its tip, so that by closing up in single file, each bird gains some welcome lift from the one in front of it. In V-formation, the inner wing gets more support than the outer one, which explains why a bird occasionally crosses over to join the other limb of the V, thereby benefiting both of its wings. Only the leading bird derives no support from the formation, so it eventually falls back to rest at the rear, while another bird takes up the front-running. Other birds, like cormorants and pelicans, derive similar mutual help by flying line abreast when they return, laden with fish, from their feeding grounds.

Often each individual alternates a few flap with a long glide, and a wave of wingbeat passes rhythmically down the line. As so often happens, man discovered that similar fue economies could be made by flying aircraft in formation, long before he realized that bird had been using the same technique.

Flapping flight achieves the highest speed found in birds. The fastest fliers tend to have a relatively narrow and sharply pointed wing appearing roughly triangular in cross section Such a wing shape contrasts sharply with the expansive wings of gliding and soaring birds which encounter tremendous air resistance and achieve at best a laboured flapping flight Among the fast flappers are the ducks and geese, pigeons and waders. Even most of ou common, small birds can get up to speeds o 30 mph (50 km/h). For sheer pace, however these pale in significance compared with the falcons and swifts, which are the fastest bird known. The Peregrine Falcon stooping to intercept its prey can reach nearly 190 mph (300 km/h), and some swifts may even attain higher speeds than this.

When we consider the speed of flight it seems all the more remarkable that birds can make a perfect touch-down on a tiny perch Clearly the main problem with landing is that the bird has to time its braking precisely enough to land without injury. If it stops too suddenly, it may stall and crash. Thus birds have to strike a vital compromise between rapid braking, and keeping airborne till the last possible moment.

The broad wings and outspread tips of the Augur Buzzard *(Buteo rufofuscus)* give it buoyancy when it hunts on the wing.

To meet the first of these demands, all birds have at their disposal various means of slowing down. The same parts of the body, which are streamlined to cleave the air so efficiently during flight, are now instinctively brought into play to increase air resistance just before alighting. The flying bird rears back into a near-vertical posture with its head held high, beats its wings forward against the direction of motion, and lowers and fans out its tail. Finally, the legs are stretched forward and relaxed just enough to absorb the jolt of landing. Wherever possible the bird also flies in below its landing place, and glides up to settle on it. In waterfowl and seabirds the webbed feet also serve as additional air brakes. Swans and other large waterbirds simply reverse their take-off procedure, and taxi in on their webbed feet.

To counteract the great loss of lift involved in using most of the wing surface as an air brake, the long feathers at the wing tips are spread out. Inasmuch as each protruding feather is modelled like the wing itself in miniature, the bird is effectively bringing into play a series of small spare wings to help ensure a soft landfall. This habit of spreading the wingtips is especially noticeable in large birds like eagles, hawks, storks, and even crows, which use it to equally good effect to facilitate gliding and soaring. The spread tail feathers also serve to maintain that little extra buoyancy needed for landing gently. Probably for the same reason, heavy-bodied birds with relatively small wings, like the Razorbill, Guillemot, and Shag, characteristically stretch out their webbed feet on either side of the tail as they glide up to a cliff ledge.

In spite of having all these devices at their disposal, not all birds are guaranteed dignified landings. As we have seen, albatrosses are well equipped for staying on the wing, and landing on firm ground is a comparatively rare event in their lives, restricted to the breeding season. Even when they marshall all their braking powers, the largest albatrosses are clumsy at landing and not infrequently go head over heels. Fortunately they are robust birds and

can usually withstand crash-landings of this sort.

So far, we have dealt with skills found to a great or lesser degree among all flying birds. However some have specialized in particularly elaborate manoeuvres. The most distinctive of these is hovering. Although it is true that this ability is possessed by many small birds such as flycatchers, finches, and sparrows, none of these can sustain such strenuous activity for more than a few seconds at a time. Skylarks, though they may appear to be hovering continuously as they pour out song high in the air, periodically close their wings so that they alternately rise and fall, rather like the undulating flight described earlier, but in a vertical plane. To find where hovering skill is developed to perfection, we have to look to those birds which depend on it for food gathering.

For some, hovering serves to poise the bird accurately over its prey, prior to swooping in for the kill. With uncanny precision, the Kestrel can hover as if suspended by a thread, its attention rivetted on some mouse or vole on the ground below. The motionless head and body are in striking contrast with the blur of the wings, which beat feverishly to and fro to maintain the bird's position. Some shrikes can perform almost as well, while Pied Kingfishers and many terns hover skilfully to locate fish.

For all their expertise, however, these birds are mere novices compared with the hummingbirds. It is one thing to modify flapping flight for hovering to focus on prey, but in the hummingbirds every aspect of the tiny body seems to have been moulded with the sole purpose of excelling at hovering flight. The compact outline of the hummingbird's wing bears little resemblance to the long, bending arms of most flying birds. Hovering with meticulous poise in front of a flower, these tiny blades whirr at a pace too fast for the human eye, enabling the bird to insert its slender bill and drink the nectar. Flitting from one flower to the next, the hummingbird displays mercurial changes of speed and direction, moving sud-

The outstretched, webbed feet of a Razorbill *(Alca torda)* may yield a little extra lift as the bird slows down to land.

denly forwards, or else straight up or down, or even backwards, with equal facility.

Only with the advent of the motion camera has it been possible to unravel the mystery of such exceptional manoeuvrability and buoyancy. In the smallest species, which weigh less than three grams, the wings beat at up to 80 strokes per second. The main plane of movement is horizontal, but on each backstroke the wing is actually flipped over, so that the tip follows a figure-of-eight path. To appreciate how this works in practice, one should imagine sweeping on outstretched arm back and forth, with the palm of the hand facing downwards on the forward stroke and upwards on the backstroke. In the flapping flight used by most birds, the upstroke produces no lift, serving merely to set up the wings for their next propulsive downbeat. By contrast, hummingbirds achieve lift on both the forward and the backward strokes, so that no motion is wasted.

Not surprisingly, such intense activity demands an enormous output of energy. To supply the flight muscles with sustaining blood, the heart beats at up to 600 times per minute, by far the fastest rate found in any bird. In many ways, therefore, we can conclude that the throbbing activity of hummingbirds has more in common with the vibrating flight of insects than of birds, and it is interesting to note that in some places, their main competitors for nectar are the so-called hummingbird hawk-moths which they so closely resemble.

Plumage and Colouration

The evolution of feathers was one of the most decisive steps in enabling birds to become such a widespread and successful group. Indeed there are few other animals whose fortunes can be so clearly linked to any one attribute as plumage in the case of birds. Feathers are a superb insulation against the cold, and allow birds to stay active in the most hostile environments. In addition, many water birds would quickly become soaked and flightless but for the excellent waterproofing qualities of plumage. Above all, however, feathers are the perfect instruments of flight, combining the lightness, strength and streamlining demanded by an airborne existence. Apart from these purely physical properties, a host of additional functions are served by the colours and shapes of feathers. The nature of this adornment is dictated partly by the sort of habitat the bird lives in, and partly by its need to advertize itself to other birds. In these respects the varying demands placed on different species has led to a great diversity of appearance which, probably more than any other single feature, accounts for man's original interest in birds and his urge to understand their behaviour.

Anyone who has plucked a fowl or duck will know that not all feathers are constructed in the same way. Most of the body is covered with contour feathers, so-called because they follow the outline of the body and to some extent define its shape. Counts of the number of these feathers on birds range from 940 in the Ruby-throated Hummingbird to 25,000 in the Whistling Swan. Each contour feather has a central shaft flanked on either side by rows of fine barbs closely packed to form a coherent web. Each barb in turn is linked to its neighbours by lots of tiny interlocking hooks. This masterful construction endows the all important wing feathers with the necessary combination of strength and flexibility to make flight possible. Inevitably, however, the sheer exertion of flight tends to prise apart the microscopic hooks, so birds periodically need to preen with the bill to close up the barbs and so tease their feathers back into shape. So while preening might appear to us a frivolous display of vanity, it is really an indispensable part of every bird's daily routine for survival.

Contour feathers are almost infinitely variable in shape and size, and suitably adorned with colour, produce some of the most striking spectacles in the bird kingdom. In the penguins, they assume their most compact form, almost reverting to the scale-like configuration of their reptilian ancestors.

Contour feathers also shape the bizarre, almost human faces of the owls, and help to adapt them for hunting successfully in total darkness, when an acute sense of hearing takes precedence over sharp vision. In some species, like the Barn Owl, the feathers radiate outwards from the bill and eyes to form a flat, round disk which presumably helps the bird to intercept the faint sounds made by rodent prey. Others, like the Long-eared and Great Horned Owl, have small erect ear tufts of feathers, unique in birds, which may assist hearing.

BELOW LEFT A dishevelled-looking, young Yellow-eyed Penguin (Megadyptes antipodes) in the process of moulting from its first downy coat into a more durable plumage of scale-like feathers.

RIGHT The facial feathers of the Long-eared Owl (Asio otus) form an elaborate disc which is thought to enhance vision and sound detection. The role in hearing, if any, played by the conspicuous ear tufts, is not known.

ABOVE The luxurious
nest of the Eider Duck
(Somateria mollissima)
is lined exclusively with
down plucked by the
female from her own
breast.

RIGHT The juvenile
Little Grey Bulbul
(Andropadus gracilis)
has soft plumes on
the head and bristles (to
assist in handling insect
prey) around the bill.

All the benefits of this ingenious feather architecture around the head would be wasted if owls themselves were noisy fliers, so the flight feathers are specially softened at the trailing edges to ensure that they cleave the air in ghostly silence. This softening effect is achieved by eliminating some of the hooks which inter-mesh to give the normal contour feather its rigidity and strength. Other birds, like the birds-of-paradise, Ostrich, egrets and Sacred Ibis, have taken this softening process to ex-tremes to provide themselves with elaborate ornamental plumes. For centuries many of these birds were relentlessly exploited to supply the millinery trade with their exotic plumage, but nowadays their use is largely con-fined to the ceremonial dress of native tribes-men.

In so-called filoplumes, the feather shaft itself has degenerated into a hair-like process. Some birds, like the aptly named Hairy-backed Bulbul, are attired with filoplumes for striking visual effect. Filoplumes also sprout at the back

of the neck in Chaffinches, some of the thrushes and warblers, and certain cormorants. In the latter, they also form distinct patches on the thighs and the back of the head, where they elongate into a conspicuous crest.

Beneath the outer layer of contour plumage, all birds are further insulated with a coat of shaftless, downy feathers. These form a speci-ally thick, soft cushion on the breasts of ducks, to help withstand the sudden impact of landing at speed on the water surface. In the breeding season, many birds are quick to exploit the insulating properties of down by lining their nests with it. The Eider Duck's nest is mostly composed of hundreds of these feathers, which the female plucks from her own breast. Simi-larly, man has long prized Eider down for bed-ding material, and it is still collected commer-cially in some countries.

The most rudimentary feathers of all are the stiff, bristle-like hairs which sprout from the base of the bill in certain birds. In flycatchers and nightjars they are thought to facilitate the

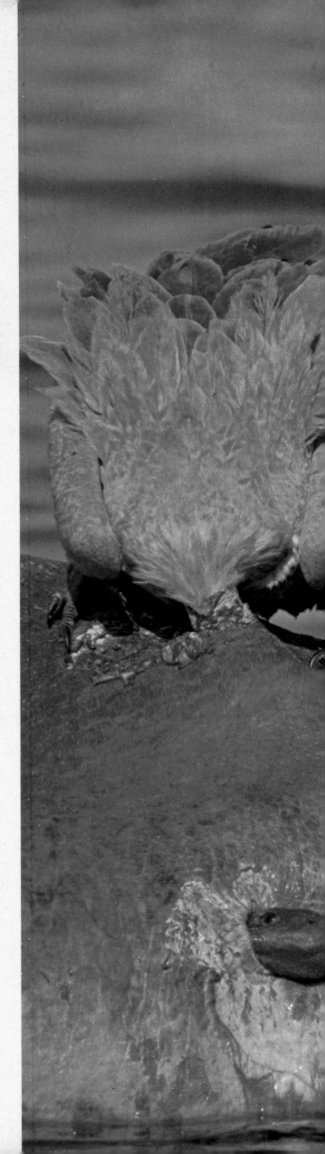

ABOVE The Plain
Nightjar *(Caprimulgus
inornatus)* hawks for
insects in the air and is
supplied with a formidable
row of long bristles to
help ensnare them.

RIGHT The carcase of a
dead hippopotamus is
breached by a group of
White-backed Vultures
(Pseudogyps africanus)
whose bald heads and
necks are specially
adapted for the task.

detection and capture of flying insects, probably by responding to touch and acting rather
like a safety net to constrain large mobile prey.
Bristles of this sort are especially well developed
in Kiwis, which are only active at night, and so
presumably find the keen sense of touch particularly useful in their search for food on the
dark forest floor.

At first sight, birds appear to be uniformly
clothed in feathers from head to tail, but this is
not always the case. Some birds have localized
bare patches, notably around the head. A particular example of this is birds that scavenge by
delving into carcasses. Thus the head and neck
of the carrion-eating storks, like the African
Maribou, and again in the vultures, are naked
except for a thin covering of down. Unattrac-
tive as this looks, it is clearly of great benefit to
these species.

Durable as feathers are, they do eventually
wear out, particularly during the breeding
season, when a considerable extra flying load
is imposed on adult birds by the demands of
foraging for a hungry brood. The need to renew
worn plumage is solved by the process called
moult, whereby the old feathers are periodically
shed and replaced by new ones. All birds moult
at least once a year, many species twice, and a
few even three times. Clearly, the loss of plumage, especially the vital flight feathers, poses
great problems for birds, since they cannot
afford to jettison their means of transport without seriously risking life and limb.

For most birds, therefore, moult is a gradual
process in which feathers are discarded one or a
few at a time as the new ones grow in. The rate
at which moult proceeds varies enormously
between different species, depending on the
extent to which they can afford to be incapaci-
tated. For example, in birds which rely heavily
on flying ability for finding and capturing prey,
moult is so prolonged as to be almost imper-
ceptible. Thus some of the large birds of prey,
especially eagles and vultures, appear to be in a
perpetual state of wing moult, shedding no
more than one or two feathers at a time so as

ABOVE The aberrant white plumage and pink eyes are characteristic of albinism in this male Blackbird *(Turdus merula)* which normally has jet black plumage and brown eyes.

ABOVE RIGHT The vivid pink colour of these Chilean Flamingos *(Phoenicopterus chilensis)* arises from pigment the birds obtain from their diet of algae and crustaceans.

BELOW RIGHT The green colour of the White-cheeked Turaco *(Tauraco leucotis)* and its red wing patches are produced by pigments found only in the Turaco family.

BELOW FAR RIGHT The soft, matt texture of the Green Pigeon's *(Treron calva)* plumage is achieved partly by the production of powder down, a cleaning agent.

not to impair their flying powers at all.

In some birds the full adult plumage is replaced at the end of the breeding season by a sombre plumage, which is worn for a time before the fresh plumage is acquired. This happens in the ducks, sunbirds and weavers, though the extent of the colour change is much more dramatic in some groups than others. The sequence of events is particularly noticeable in drakes, which temporarily change their often colourful plumage early in the breeding season for a garb that more closely resembles the drab plumage of the ducks. They retain their duller appearance for three to seven months according to species. However, the most remarkable feature of this moult is that the males shed all of their primary and secondary wing feathers at once, and are rendered temporarily flightless. Obviously this is an especially hazardous time for them, and they take no part in raising the young, but instead take refuge in the open sea or retire to thick cover till they regain a full complement of feathers and once again emerge capable of flight. Simultaneous moult of all the wing quills also occurs in the flamingos, grebes, divers, rails and darters.

Some species faced with such a drastic moult undertake a special migration to find somewhere safe. After the breeding season, many Shelduck, both ducks and drakes, fly from Britain and north-west Europe to the sandbanks of the Heligoland Bight, where they spend a flightless period of about a month in comparative safety, before returning to their breeding grounds for the remainder of the year. In Swans, the flightless period is even longer, lasting for six to seven weeks.

A widespread form of localized moult occurs in the breeding season, when many birds which are about to incubate lose some of their down feathers below the breast, so that the contour feathers merely shield from view one, two or more bare patches of skin. These brood patches are richly supplied with blood vessels, so that body heat can be transferred rapidly from the incubating parents to their eggs. However, this adaptation is not universal, and some birds like cormorants and gannets do not develop brood patches. Instead, gannets keep their single egg warm with their webbed feet, which house an extensive network of blood vessels for this purpose.

As feathers wear out, they also become faded and lustreless, so moult further ensures that birds maintain a bright, colourful appearance. In birds we find colour developed to a higher degree than in any other animals, with the possible exception of certain coral reef fishes and tropical insects. The reason for this is not hard to find; unlike the other dominant group on land, the mammals, birds have a poor sense of smell, and instead they explore and understand their surroundings principally by vision. As a result, visual appearance has come to play a fundamental role in the day to day communication between birds.

It is only in recent years that we have been able to fully answer the apparently simple question of how a bird happens to be coloured the way it is. Colours are produced in a variety of highly subtle ways. Some originate from pigments, while others result from the fine structure of the feather itself. The blacks, greys, browns and buff colours so common in birds are due to the most widespread pigments in the animal kingdom. A dense concentration of this substance in the feathers is responsible for the typical jet black dress of crows, European Blackbirds, and certain game birds. In modified form this pigment also produces a red-brown or even yellow colour, such as we find in the downy coats of domestic chicks.

However, most yellows, oranges and reds are due to a different pigment, which birds cannot produce for themselves but have to obtain from their diet. The vivid carmine and pink plumage of flamingos is thus derived from the microscopic algae and shrimps they feed on, and in captivity the birds have to be supplied with their natural food, or else a specially pigmented substitute to maintain their colour intensity. If canaries are deprived of a suitable diet, their characteristic 'natural' yellow appearance gradually fades, and they become white. Even among wild birds, we occasionally find such albino individuals that cannot produce their natural pigment in all or part of their plumage, no matter how well they are fed. The yellow and red pigments, however, affect more than just the plumage of birds; they are also responsible for the fleshy, red wattles of pheasants, and even the bright red egg yolks of the Gentoo Penguin.

Just as an artist mixes his palette to create a greater range of colours, so birds can combine these simple pigments to produce subtle intermediate hues. From a dense mosaic of tiny black and yellow spots emerges the soft olive-green plumage of Greenfinches and some members of the tit family. The green colour of the Mallard Duck's bill is also produced in this way. In fact, pure green pigment has only been discovered in one group of birds, a fruit-eating African family called the Turacos. The amount of this special green colouration seems to be related

to the lushness of the vegetation in which the birds live, being most evident in those that inhabit evergreen tropical forest. Another pigment unique to some Turacos produces blazing crimson patches on the wings.

As far as we know, the true greens of other birds are produced not by pigment but by the structure of the feathers themselves, which scatters the light that falls on them. In a similar way, the earth's atmosphere scatters sunlight to make the sky look blue. This is a very widespread source of colour in birds, creating not only greens but also blues, violets and even white. It is responsible for the brilliant colours of kingfishers, bee-eaters, tanagers, and parrots, to name but a few.

Some of our most gaudy birds are distinguished by iridescent colours, which change with the angle of view like the bloom on a soap bubble or a pool of oil. This phenomenon is again associated with the structure of the feathers. In many birds the plumage is iridescent all over, which lends it a bright metallic

sheen, ranging from the ebony gloss of crows
to the shimmering colours of the Peacock, some
of the American orioles and the African glossy
starlings. Even the Common Starling, unwelcome urban dweller as it often is, looks un-
deniably handsome at close quarters, with all
the colours of the rainbow arrayed at the tips
of its neck and breast feathers.

In other species, iridescent colours are confined to distinct regions of the body, often with
striking results. Ducks have a metallic wing
flash of blue, green or gold, which often contrasts vividly with an otherwise drab plumage.
Most spectacular of all, however, are the
brilliant patches of iridescence that adorn
birds-of-paradise, hummingbirds, and sunbirds, especially on the crown and throat where
the feathers often form a glittering shield. In
flight, these shimmer with a gem-like intensity
unrivalled amongst birds. Scarcely less colourful are the Pittas, or Jewel-thrushes, resplen-
dent in a lacquered plumage best known for its
reds, violets and cobalt blue.

Feathers are not always made with the
express purpose of highlighting colour in the
ways described. On the contrary, the plumage
of some birds has a distinctly matt look, as if the
feathers were covered with a thin film of dust.
This effect is produced by the disintegration of
the down feathers into a fine powder, which
the bird then uses to clean its plumage, just as
other birds have occasional dust baths or water
baths for the same purpose. Powder down, as it
is called, is only found in certain groups of
birds, notably the herons, toucans, parrots,
bower-birds, and pigeons, and typically occurs
only in patches. While somewhat lacking the
extravagance of iridescent plumage, powder
down gives these birds a rare softness and
subtlety of colour. Some birds-of-paradise
show velvety patches of plumage, but in this
case the texture is produced by short feathers
standing perpendicularly from the skin.

Having used all the colour possibilities of
pigment and feather structure, one last source
of embellishment remains at a bird's disposal,

namely the secretions of the oil gland, which almost every bird has concealed beneath the feathers at the top of the tail. In the course of preening, birds use the oil from this gland as a conditioning agent, working it through their plumage to keep it soft, pliable and waterproof; the special advantages of this to water birds scarcely need stressing. In certain birds the oil is coloured, and its transfer to the plumage imparts a characteristic tint. In the Great Indian Hornbill, the basically white wing feathers thus become yellowish, while in some gulls, terns and pelicans, the pink tinge on the breast may also originate in this way. For obvious reasons, this special source of adornment in birds is aptly called cosmetic colouration.

Having established how birds come to be coloured, there remains the question of why such a diversity of colour patterns is necessary at all. Colour is rarely just a lavish display of ornamentation. Sometimes it is a kind of uniform, that signifies the individual's rank in the population to which it belongs. Most birds spend a certain period of adolescence before they gain sexual maturity. These immature birds are usually distinguished by having a more sombre dress than the adults. Apart from indicating their subordinate status to older birds, such plumage probably also prevents younger birds from being too conspicuous to predators at a time when their lack of experience in the wild places them at special risk.

Most small birds such as the finches, buntings, warblers and tits live on average only a year or two at the most (although potentially they can and have been known to live up to nine or ten years), so there is a great need for young birds to enter the breeding population as quickly as possible. In these circumstances, the plumage of immature birds usually differs little from that of the adults, and may only persist for a few months before it is moulted and replaced with breeding dress. The transition is much slower in long-lived species, which include many birds of prey, freshwater birds, and seabirds. Grey Herons, for example,

have been known to live as long as 25 years, Herring Gulls for over 30 years, and the Royal Albatross for 30–40 years. In ideal conditions of captivity even longer lifespans have been recorded; one Eagle Owl, for instance, lived 68 years in an aviary. In general, the duration of adolescence is proportional to the expected lifespan, so that many large gulls, gannets, divers, and storks first breed at three to four years old, eagles at four to six years, and some albatrosses not till they are at least seven. Immature birds of these species may pass through several successive plumage types, each one progressively more like the adult, till they finally moult into full breeding plumage. As an illustration, the immature Herring Gull is typically a mottled and streaky brown for its first year, and gradually acquires increasing amounts of white and grey during the three-year transition to breeding plumage.

Once adulthood is reached, the male and female may look exactly alike, both being equally dull or brightly coloured. Alternatively, the sexes may differ markedly in appearance, with the male usually more strikingly coloured. Indeed female birds-of-paradise are so soberly attired compared with their exotically plumed mates that in early museum collections the two sexes of a single species were sometimes described as separate species. Often the divergent colour patterns arise from a different blend of pigments, so that the male and female European Blackbird, for example, are black and brown respectively. The function of such differences probably lies in the greater proportion of hazardous nesting duties performed by the female, so that she benefits from being less conspicuous to predators. However, in a small number of species – the phalaropes, painted snipe, and button-quails – the male undertakes the bulk of incubation and brood care and, in keeping with this reversal of the sex roles, the female is the more brightly coloured member of the pair.

Even in adulthood the plumage colour does not always stay the same, especially among birds which live in regions where the climate is strongly seasonal. In such regions there is usually a specially favourable time of the year for breeding, and it is at this time that birds have to attire themselves in colourful, decorative plumage to look their best. In temperate regions some species, particularly the more flamboyant males, lose some of the hallmarks of their breeding dress in the winter when they can afford to look less attractive. Thus the Black-headed Gull sports a dashing chocolate-

ABOVE The plumage colour of immature seabirds is usually more drab than that of the adults. Here an adult Glaucous Gull (*Larus hyperboreus*) (right) contrasts with its offspring.

RIGHT Like vultures, the Marabou Stork's (*Leptoptilos crumeniferus*) naked head and neck indicate that it is a scavenger for carrion. A dangling throat pouch adds to the grotesque profile.

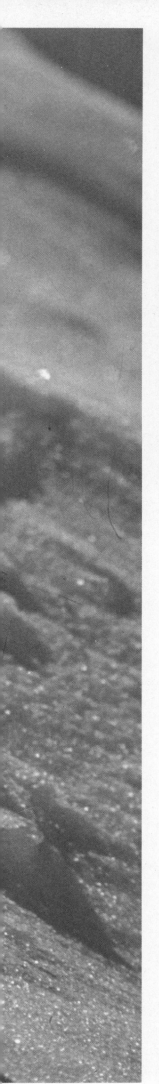

LEFT Camouflage: the Ptarmigan turns white in the winter.

ABOVE Sandgrouse are coloured to match their desert background.

coloured head or hood in the summer, but in winter the head is almost white. Similarly, egrets shed their long ornamental plumes for the winter when they are least needed.

Some of these changes are more obviously associated with seasonal differences. In northern latitudes, where a blanket of snow annually transforms the dark summer landscape, the Ptarmigan and Willow Grouse follow suit, switching from a brown breeding dress to a coat of almost pure white in the winter. Even in relatively constant environments, the need for concealment is a major factor in determining the plumage colour of many birds. Ground-nesting species are particularly vulnerable to predation, and provide some of the best examples of colour-matching with the background.

In highly exposed desert habitats birds are obliged to nest on the ground, and it is not surprising to find that they are almost invariably pale in colour, depending on white, grey, and ochre to blend themselves in with the landscape. Notable examples include the coursers, certain bustards, sandgrouse and larks. Where the species has an extensive range embracing a variety of substrate colours, its plumage pattern often varies accordingly to give the best colour match for the particular terrain concerned. This is best illustrated by the North African Desert Lark, whose colour shows a remarkable similarity to whatever sort of desert soil the bird frequents. In Central Arabia, patches of black lava adjoin areas of almost pure white

sand, and are, in turn, inhabited by a very dark and a distinctly pale race of the species. Apparently nothing will induce the pale birds to stray on to the black sand nor the dark birds to encroach on the pale sand.

Sharp contrasts in colour are typically lacking in most desert-dwelling birds, but this is not always so. The Cream-coloured Courser, a familiar bird of stony arid country bordering the Sahara Desert, is basically sandy in colour, but this is disrupted by a number of striking dark bars on its head, and black ends to the wings visible in flight. We normally associate such colour patterns with habitats like pebbly ground and rocky shores, where the background is sufficiently varied to render a plainly coloured bird more conspicuous. By adopting a subtle pattern of stripes, streaks and patches, the bird thus seeks to break up its outline and so appear at one with its surroundings.

The rich mosaic of light, shade and colour on a woodland floor offers one of the best situations for camouflage of this kind. Few ground-nesting birds are harder to detect than the Woodcock whose blend of brown, black, buff and yellow is a perfect tapestry of its surroundings. In common with many like-coloured gamebirds, disguise is the Woodcock's best means of nest defence; the eggs are concealed by the bird sitting so tightly that it will only flush from them if a predator is inches away and discovery inevitable.

If any group of birds surpasses the Woodcock in this kind of camouflage then it must be

the nightjars, a widespread family which like to nest on the ground amongst scattered pieces of bark, twig and dead leaves. Once on the nest, a Nightjar flattens itself to the ground to avoid casting a shadow, sits absolutely still as if frozen, and so effectively merges with its background. When danger threatens it still has a few ruses in reserve, closing its eyes to the merest slits to avoid betraying any tell-tale glint. Nightjars are active mainly at twilight and dusk when they hawk for insects. During the day they either perch on the ground as if on the nest, or crouch along the limb of a tree, and become virtually indistinguishable from the bark. This method of disguise is perfectly developed in the Nightjar's close relatives, the potoos of South and Central America, and the frogmouths of Asia and Australia. The Great Potoo lays its single egg on top of a broken tree-stump and adopts a stiffly erect posture when incubating. Frogmouths prefer to build a flimsy nest of sticks on the horizontal fork of a tree, and the incubating bird appropriately assumes a frozen, angled posture, with its head stretched upwards, so that it resembles a broken branch.

Such precise matching of colour and behaviour to the background vegetation is not, however, confined to woodland birds. The Bittern is a close relative of the herons, living a secretive solitary life in dense reed beds. The plumage, especially on the neck, breast and back, is vertically striped with alternate bands of brown and yellow which closely resemble a background of dead reeds. Bitterns are famous for enhancing their cryptic colouration with a variety of unique postures and movements. When danger threatens, the bird becomes quite rigid, with the bill and neck pointed stiffly skywards and the feathers tightly pressed against the body to emphasize its reed-like colour pattern. The bird faces the source of danger, watching attentively with staring yellow eyes angled downwards, and turns slowly, or else swivels at great speed, to follow any movement of the observer. Some species will even sway gently with the reeds in a light breeze.

Birds, therefore, often use camouflage as a first line of defence, hoping that it will prevent them from being noticed at all. If cryptic colouration fails, however, and the bird is directly threatened, it may resort to using its plumage as a means of visual intimidation. To take an example, the Snowy Owl lives in the frozen Arctic tundra and adopts a camouflage of snow white plumage throughout the year. The bird is at greatest risk when sitting on its nest which is built on open ground, usually on a raised vantage point. Intruders are confronted with a fierce display in which the owl glares fixedly, spreads its wings, and fluffs its feathers so that it seems to be twice as big as it really is. The young owls in the nest adopt the same posture, as do the chicks of Fulmar Petrels.

Some small owls have developed a most ingenious device for deflecting would-be predators. The owl's strategy is simply to deceive us into thinking that it has eyes at the back of

its head, in order to deter any attack from behind. This ruse is found in the African Pearl-spotted Owlet, and the American Pygmy Owl, which have two remarkably life-like false eyes and even the semblance of a beak at the back of the head, etched in black and white feathers.

Conspicuous patches of colour, depicting no particular shape, are also employed by many birds to signal their presence and pinpoint their position to other individuals of the same species. Many flocking birds, particularly waders, have distinctive white patches on the wings, rump or tail which serve to ensure contact between members of the flock, especially in flight. Similarly, the white plumage of many seabirds, such as gannets, gulls and terns, may help birds to locate others who have discovered a plentiful source of food. On a sunny day, the feverish hovering of a tern which has chanced on a shoal of fish can be detected from considerable distances by the flashing of its white wings.

In dense forest, just as in the open sea, birds have the same problem of making contact with other members of their own species. Many woodland birds, therefore, like the Redstart, jays, and woodpeckers, bear conspicuous patches of white or red, usually on the rump or tail, since these are best placed to advertize the bird's position to any following it.

These examples should make it clear that we cannot ascribe any single function to the colours of birds. In most cases, the bird strikes the best compromise between being visible and attractive to its own species, and being inconspicuous, or even frightening, to other animals that might threaten its survival.

ABOVE With these eye spots at the back of its head, the African Pearl-spotted Owlet (*Glaucidium perlatum*) hopes to appear vigilant in all directions.

RIGHT The conspicuous white undersides and rumps of this wader flock serve a signalling function, helping individuals to maintain contact with one another.

Food and Feeding Habits

An adequate food supply is basic to any animal's survival. Food provides the body with the energy it needs to maintain good condition, to stay mobile and, in warm-blooded creatures like birds, to keep the body temperature at a constant level.

As we have seen, the demands of flight have dominated the evolution of body shape in birds; they have gained mastery of the air by striking a delicate compromise between minimizing weight and maximizing strength and power. While a bird needs lots of food to fuel its strenuous flight, it cannot afford to undo the benefits of a light airframe, either by burdening itself with bulky feeding apparatus, or by salting away large body reserves of energy. Thus the head is small compared with the total bulk of the body, and conspicuously lacks the elaborate chewing mechanism typical of animals that lead a more leisurely existence. Birds have long since abandoned heavy jawbones and teeth, and instead the horny bill and mouth are used primarily for manipulating food, and breaking or tearing it up, mostly in a rudimentary fashion. The major task of grinding up food has been relegated to the gizzard, a muscular pulverizing part of the stomach. In species that eat tough seeds and plant material, the milling action of the gizzard is often assisted by grit and small stones which the bird deliberately swallows for this purpose. Other birds make similar use of the hard parts of the food they eat, like shells of molluscs, or fruit stones. These materials are also valuable for the minerals they contain. Even with a powerful gizzard, certain birds, especially birds of prey such as hawks and falcons, and also owls, inevitably accumulate more indigestible material than they can put to good use, and periodically have to regurgitate the excess in pellet form. These pellets may be bound with the prey's fur or feathers mixed with its bones, like those of owls, so that they retain their shape for some time, or may be so loosely bound, as with the chitinous remains of flies which have been cast up by the Spotted Flycatcher, as to disintegrate almost at once.

There is also a great need for rapid digestion to supply a steady flow of energy for sustaining flight. In the Cedar Waxwing, for example, as little as sixteen minutes may elapse between eating a berry and excreting the indigestible stone. Not surprisingly, therefore, birds, particularly the smaller ones, are compulsive eaters and, at particularly demanding times like chick-rearing and just prior to migration, all birds have to devote most of the day to searching for food. It is only at such times that birds are known to lay down body stores of fat, as a source of fuel surplus to immediate needs. Only flightless birds, however, can afford to accumulate permanent reserves of this kind. For flying birds, this reserve can never be big enough to cater for more than a brief period of exceptional energy demands. In general they must rely on finding enough food each day to support their active spells, and to last them through the night. Birds are often unable to fortify themselves even in this way against excessive stress, and death by starvation is not uncommon. Nor is this fate confined to birds in harsh environments. Thus the Quelea, a small African passerine which breeds in huge colonies, is occasionally found weak and helpless in its roosting spot at dawn, having expended too much energy keeping warm during the relatively long tropical night to go forth in search of food at daybreak.

Many birds would find it impossible to survive were it not for the crop, a thin sac-like extension of the digestive tract on the underside of the throat. This is essentially a temporary food reservoir which the bird can fill—and draw on later—when the stomach is stretched to capacity. The crop is especially well developed in pigeons, parrots, and game birds which specialize in a bulky vegetable diet. Such food is often available only in rather exposed habitats, where there is a grave risk of being discovered by a predator. By stuffing its crop, a bird can therefore retire to a less conspicuous place to digest its meal in safety. The

RIGHT A Green Woodpecker *(Picus viridis)* at its nest hole, using its stiff tail to brace it upright. This species spends much of its time on the ground, probing for ants.

crop is also particularly useful for tiding birds over long, cold winter nights, and for storing the additional food needed to raise a brood.

Birds eat practically every kind of food available to them, although naturally enough there is a strong bias towards diets that provide a high ratio of energy to bulk. While some birds eat exclusively animal or vegetable food, just as many others have a mixed diet. Some birds exploit seasonal and geographical variations in food, turning to new resources as they become available. Many finches and buntings, for instance, are predominantly seed-eaters in the winter, but switch to insect prey in the spring and summer. Often such a change is associated with the onset of the breeding season, since a protein-rich insect diet allows the nestlings to develop faster, and the parents to cope with the extra effort of catering for a hungry brood. However, in many birds the food taken by the adults may differ from that given to the young. Often the adults take a mixed diet, or even a mainly vegetable one, while feeding their nestlings with insects or other animal food.

The best indication of what sort of food a bird eats is often the shape of its beak. There seems no limit to the variety of forms this structure has assumed for handling different sorts of food. In part this is due to the varied functions the bill has to perform. It not only has to pick up food, or grasp and immobilize living prey, but often has to be able to tear it up or crack it open. Moreover, a bird may not want to eat its food on the spot, especially if it has chicks to feed. The bill then has to be big enough and strong enough to carry back to the nest one or several items, sometimes over relatively long distances. Birds that feed on prey which is hidden below the surface of the ground, wood, or water, have to depend on the bill for probing and sensing when it has located something edible. For this reason, the bill, superficially a somewhat inert structure, is always provided with sensory organs, especially of touch. This tactile sense is especially well developed in the bill-tips of woodpeckers, ducks, and waders.

Perhaps the best-known of all bill profiles belongs to the birds of prey, whose powerful hooked beaks and long talons are impressive equipment for seizing, killing and tearing up prey. The larger eagles have a remarkably strong bite for getting a firm grasp on their quarry and for dismembering it. The Harpy Eagle probably wins the distinction of having the largest and most formidable bill of all predatory birds. An inhabitant of the Amazonian forests, it hunts sloths and monkeys, which it plucks out of the tree canopy with its powerful talons. Other eagles hunt for prey almost as large, such as prairie dogs and small antelopes. Occasional killers of domestic sheep, like the Golden Eagle, are much maligned, since the bulk of their diet is composed of smaller mammals like rabbits and hares, and when they do select a lamb, it is often a weak animal that would have died anyway.

The hawks are close relatives of the eagles, but being smaller they specialize in lesser prey

ABOVE The North American Cedar Waxwing *(Bombycilla cedrorum)* has a staple diet of berries and small fruits.

ABOVE LEFT A Barn Owl *(Tyto alba)* returns to deliver a vole to its young.

LEFT An immature African Fish Eagle *(Haliaeetus vocifer)* dismembers a fish which it caught in its talons.

OVERLEAF African Darters or Anhingas *(Anhinga rufa)* holding out their wings to dry after a bout of fishing.

like rodents, lizards, frogs and large insects. The Osprey lives on a diet of fish, hence the American name of Fish-Hawk. With measured wingbeats, it slowly quarters the water high above the surface, before plunging downwards to grasp a fish in its talons. The sorts of food taken by hawks also form the mainstay of the owls' diet. Though unrelated to eagles and hawks, the owls are similarly endowed with hooked beaks for killing and tearing prey. Most of them are adapted for stealthy nocturnal hunting, with large orb-like eyes, an acute sense of hearing, and specially softened flight feathers that row noiselessly through the night air.

Inevitably there are raptors whose victims are other birds. This is the speciality of some of the falcons (and also some of the hawks) which are renowned for their skill and swiftness of flight. There are few aerial spectacles more breath-taking than the lightning stoop of the Peregrine Falcon to seize or strike with its talons a hapless duck or wader. Even poisonous snakes are tackled by several birds of prey. The

most celebrated of these is the Secretary Bird, which elegantly stalks the African plains on long legs protected by a thick coat of feathers. Surprising a snake, it strikes forward and pounds its victim to death with powerful, sledge-hammer blows of its feet.

Some of the most intriguing birds of the African and South American plains and mountains are, however, the vultures, whose menacing hooked beaks, long necks, and relatively weak feet, equip them for scavenging on carcases rather than catching their own prey. The most famous and largest is the Andean Condor, with a wingspan exceeding nine feet (three metres). Though classically held to be lazy birds, exploiting the hard work of others, recent studies in East Africa have shown that most of the mammals fed on by vultures die of disease or hunger, and are not, in fact, those killed by predators. Thus the vultures do an invaluable job of clearing the plains of carrion, and some have evolved surprisingly intelligent feeding methods. The Lammergeier breaks open

41

ABOVE A handsome
Secretary Bird
(Sagittarius serpentarius)
skins a snake which it
first stomped to death
with its feet.

RIGHT White Pelicans
(Pelecanus onocrotalus)
engaged in a cooperative
fishing strategy. A small
group of individuals
bands into a horseshoe
over a shoal and, keeping
in formation, the birds
swim along, periodically
dipping their gaping
bills in unison to engulf
ambushed fish.

ABOVE RIGHT Egyptian
Vultures *(Neophron
percnopterus),* like the
juvenile bird shown here,
have learned to crack
open nutritious Ostrich
eggs with stones.

bones by dropping them on to rocks from a
great height, and then gleans the marrow from
the splintered fragments. Even more remarkable is the recently discovered behaviour of the
Egyptian Vulture, which is known to get at the
contents of Ostrich eggs by dropping stones on
the tough shell, which it could not otherwise
break. As we shall see, such tool-using is rare
in the bird kingdom.

Quite unrelated to the birds described above,
but equally voracious predators of small birds,
lizards, rodents and insects, is the diminutive
thrush-sized shrike family. With its robust
beak, the Great Grey Shrike seizes its victim,
and often indulges in the macabre habit of
impaling it on a thorn or even the barb of a wire
fence, so creating a food larder which earns it
the popular name of butcher bird in England.
(This name is also given to the Red-backed
Shrike, which unlike the Great Grey Shrike,
breeds in England.)

Fish-eating birds usually have long pointed
bills, rather like forceps, to gain a firm purchase

on their prey. The fish is rarely speared,
although this is apparently how the Anhinga,
or Darter, secures its prey, when an underwater pursuit culminates in a snake-like forward thrust of the bird's neck. In most other
fish-eaters, the prey is caught between the
mandibles, and thereafter various devices ensure that the slippery victim is firmly grasped.
Herons and mergansers have sharp serrations
on the margins of the beak, while other birds,
like the cormorants and shearwaters, have
long, cutting beaks with a small hook at the tip
to help retain the prey till it can be swallowed
at the surface. Pelicans also have a bill of this
sort, but are further endowed with a massive
gape and distensible pouch akin to a trawl-net.

Many fish-eating birds pursue their prey
underwater, strongly propelled by webbed
feet, paddle-like wings, or a combination of the
two. The best-prepared for this role are the
penguins, whose streamlined bodies make them
such excellent swimmers that they have little
need of any special bill adaptations for retain-

ing the prey. So at home are they in their marine environment that they can stay submerged for long periods, swallowing several fish before surfacing. Amongst the diving auks, the Puffin sports one of the best known beaks of all birds. His powerful, brightly-coloured bill can hold several fish at a time, each one laid crosswise between the tongue and the lower mandible, so that the beak can be opened to catch more.

Herons and egrets depend on the element of surprise, standing like statues in shallow water, or wading with measured steps, before striking with lightning speed at an unsuspecting fish. One of the most remarkable strategies is employed by the African Black Heron, which slowly stalks through the water and periodically fans its wings forwards over its head. This effectively forms a parasol to blot out the sun, and so shadows the surface below to help it see its prey.

One of the most spectacular and bizarre bills among birds that hunt by wading belongs to

the aptly named Shoebill. The upper mandible is a massive, bulging affair, hooked at the tip, with which the bird lunges at fish that come within reach. The bill is also thought to be used like a powerful awl for digging out lungfish concealed in muddy lake-beds.

Other fish-eating birds detect their prey from a suitable vantage point above the water's surface. Kingfishers have long spear-like bills, and mostly lie in wait on overhanging perches, plunging to seize a small fish from the shallows, whence they return to their stance, often to batter the struggling victim on a branch before swallowing it.

The terns go one step further and actively hover above the water surface, diving head-long when they spot a fish, and submerging briefly before reappearing with it firmly held in a pincer-grip. Some terns dip gracefully to the water, scarcely breaking the surface. Among the best practitioners of surface fishing are undoubtedly the skimmers, close allies of the terns. These remarkable-looking birds are

ABOVE During the chick-rearing period the Puffin *(Fratercula arctica)* reduces the number of trips it has to make to and from the feeding grounds by collecting several fish at a time in its bill.

LEFT The Kingfisher *(Alcedo atthis)* plunge dives for fish from a suitable vantage point. The fish are always swallowed head first so this one will have to be turned round.

RIGHT An inhabitant of the papyrus marshes of the Upper Nile, the bizarre Shoebill *(Balaeniceps rex)* delves with its bill for lungfish in the mud and shallows.

unique in having a deep, blade-like lower mandible, which is markedly longer than the upper one. Hunting above the water, by night as well as by day, the skimmer repeatedly glides down to skim for some yards along the surface, delicately ploughing the water with its lower mandible. When contact is made with a fish, the upper mandible closes to hold it firm.

Many birds have evolved feeding habits to take advantage of the myriads of small organisms other than fish that abound in the rich surface waters of rivers and lakes. The opportunity to cream off this abundant food supply has led to some of the most sophisticated kinds of feeding apparatus found in birds. Most belong to the group called waders, whose length of leg generally determines how far they can forage from the shore. The graceful Avocet is a relatively small but long-legged wader, frequenting shallow lakes, marshes and pools, where it catches small creatures in the surface slime by sweeping a slender upcurved bill from side to side with a regular scything motion. In deeper water Avocets immerse their heads and up-end like dabbling ducks.

To emphasize the diversity of bill shape in the wader family, the Curlew's bill arches downwards even more strongly than the Avocet's does upwards. These birds, along with the straight-billed godwits and snipes, feed by probing mud and soft soil for small animals. Success in this search is ensured by the provision of well-developed sense organs at the tip of the bill, which tell the bird when it has made contact with something edible.

The name of the Spoonbill defines its most characteristic feature, a long bill shaped like two flattened spoons. Dipping the partly-open bill vertically into the water, they sweep it to and fro, snapping it shut on contact with suitable prey.

However, the aristocrats of this feeding level are the flamingos, tall, gaudy birds with long, sinuous necks and spindly legs ending in webbed feet. Their seemingly ugly bill is unique among birds, being sharply bent so that it appears to be broken in half. The lower mandible is deep and trough-shaped, the upper one small like a lid. When feeding, a flamingo tramples the mud to stir it up, and immerses its head so that the bill points backwards. Water is then sucked in, often by vigorous gobbling movements, and tiny plants and crustaceans strained off by the fine, hair-like processes which line the bill. Congregating in vast flocks to feed, flamingos make a blaze of pink and red plumage which ranks as one of the most exciting spectacles to be seen in the wild.

Many of the water birds described above will eat insect larvae and insects too, but we have to look to dry land to find the truly insectivorous species of birds. Insects present such a varied and abundant food supply that a great many birds, representing several different families, have specialized in their capture. Some of the most highly adapted insect-eaters are designed for catching flying insects. For this, their bills are relatively broad, ensuring a wide gape, and are often fringed with stout bristles to help trap

prey. The swallows, martins, swifts and night-jars have, to varying degrees, abandoned contact with the ground, and instead are superbly built for spending long periods in the air, where they hunt with unparalleled speed and manoeuvrability. Their squat bills have a prodigious gape for scooping up flying insects. During the breeding season, swifts often forage for many miles from their nest-sites, amassing a compact bolus of insects for later regurgitation to their young.

LEFT Lesser Flamingos (*Phoeniconaias minor*) feeding in Lake Nakuru.

BELOW The Avocet (*Avosetta recurvirostra*) sweeps its upturned bill from side to side to sift food from the water.

BOTTOM The Spoonbill (*Platalea leucorodia*).

49

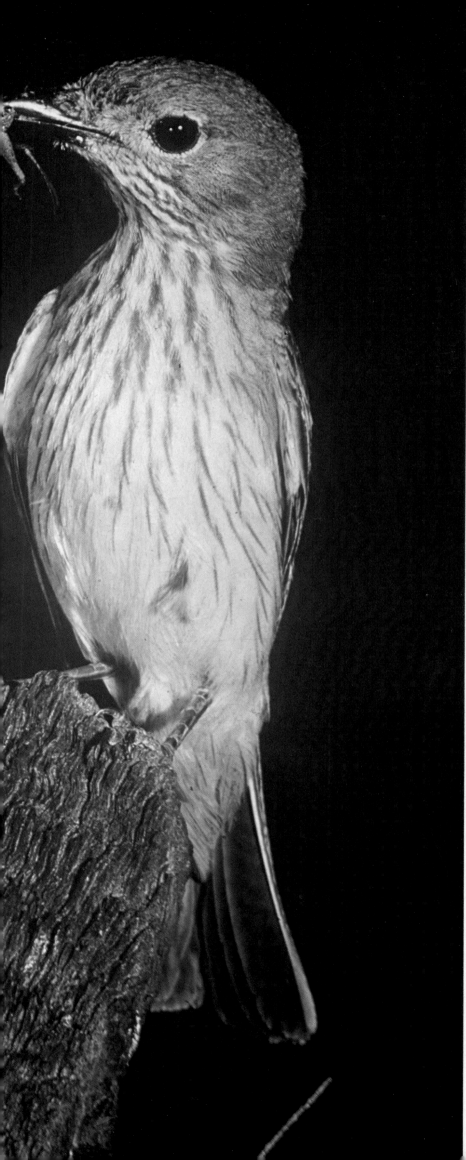

Insects which live among foliage, and on the branches and trunks of trees, are sought by a legion of small birds, such as tits, wrens, and warblers, whose tireless hunting behaviour is a familiar sight in woods and gardens. Their bills are like fine forceps, ideal for gleaning insects that adhere to the surface of leaves and stems.

The woodpeckers, however, must rank as the most interesting of woodland dwellers. Hopping like clockwork up a tree, the bird braces itself against the trunk with strong feet and specially stiffened tail feathers, and then hammers the wood with its formidable chisel of a bill. Chips flying, the bird gradually drills down to its prey, which it unearths by extruding an enormously long tongue, armed at the tip with lethal barbs. Other woodpeckers hunt on the ground, probing with their tongues into insect burrows and similar cavities to catch or collect insects.

There are no birds which actually eat wood, although all other plant resources are utilized. The American Sapsucker drills, woodpecker-style, to mop up sap with its brush-tipped tongue. Leaves and shoots are eaten by many gamebirds, like the Capercaillie, which prospers on a spartan diet of pine needles. Vegetable matter is also the mainstay of many ducks, geese and swans, which graze on grass and aquatic plants.

The seasonal progression of plants, from flowering to fruit or seed, is exploited throughout by a host of birds, including some of the most exotic species we know. The brilliantly coloured hummingbirds flit effortlessly from flower to flower, hovering with extraordinary precision before inserting a long, slender bill and extracting the nectar along a pipette-like tongue. While some of the honey-eaters of the Australasian region also feed on nectar, all of the nectar-feeders also take other foods, usually insects as a source of protein, or even fruit. The latter is a prolific resource in tropical regions, and is exploited by a great variety of pigeons, doves, cotingas and tanagers. Best known are the hornbills and toucans, whose massive, vivid bills are sometimes as long as the body itself. The function of such an elaborate tool is still something of a mystery, though it must help these rather ungainly birds to pluck awkwardly placed fruits as well as probably being important in display.

Finally, plants supply a specially rich energy source in the form of seeds and nuts, which meet the needs of many species in cold as well as hot climates. In the tropics, the parrots are the most characteristic seed-eaters, and scarcely need further description. The most widespread

52

group of seed-eaters, however, are the finches, buntings, grassfinches and weavers, small birds in which different species have independently hit upon many solutions to the problem of cracking open seeds and nuts. The Hawfinch has muscular mandibles that work against each other like a pair of anvils. In this way, they can crush the hardest cherry stones with deceptive ease for a bird that tips the scales at only two ounces. The beak of the Crossbill is, as we might guess, crossed at the tips for severing cones and stripping off the scales to extract the seeds with the surgical precision of a scalpel. Lastly among the finches, it is fitting to note a unique deviant, which must qualify as the greatest exponent in the art of tool-using mentioned earlier. The cunning of Galapagos Woodpecker Finch has abandoned seed-eating on discovering that, by gripping a cactus spine or small twig in its bill, it can probe into crevices and winkle out insects and grubs.

The strangest feeding habits of all surely belong to the honeyguides, small birds whose somewhat drab appearance belies their remarkable behaviour. They live in tropical forest and savannah in Africa and Asia, where they feed on wasps, bees, other insects and, uniquely, on beeswax, which they raid from hives. Their taste for wax was first noted in 1569 by a Portuguese missionary, who complained that honeyguides came to feed on the candles he placed on the altar of his church. Stranger still, to get at otherwise inaccessible beeswax, honeyguides have learned to enlist the help of African honey-badgers and even man. Presumably the original association was formed with honey-badgers, and man has since collaborated with the birds for mutual gain. Those who have studied honeyguides think it most likely that the bird starts looking for a bees' nest after it has attracted the attention of a man or a honey-badger. On finding one, the bird begins to advertize itself vigorously by loud churrings, and continuing to display like this, blazes a trail for the accomplice to follow. In this way, the bird eventually guides the robber

ABOVE LEFT A Galapagos Woodpecker Finch (*Camarhynchus pallidus*) uses a cactus spine to probe for insects and larvae in a dead branch.

FAR LEFT Like the New World hummingbirds, the Old World sunbirds feed on nectar but they cannot hover so well and more often perch to feed, like this Orange-breasted Sunbird (*Nectarinia violacea*).

LEFT The Crossbill's (*Loxia curvirostra*) beak is crossed over at the tips for stripping cones and extracting the seeds.

ABOVE The Capercaillie (*Tetrao urogallus*) lives on a diet of pine needles.

53

BELOW In a remarkable case of cooperation between quite unrelated animals, the Greater Honeyguide *(Indicator indicator)* leads honey-badgers and men to bee's nests, and then shares in the spoils.

RIGHT Blue Tits *(Parus caeruleus)* have learned to pierce milk bottle tops to get at the cream inside.

to the bees' nest, signalling its location by perching in silence and waiting patiently till the badger or man has broken into the nest and exposed the honeycombs. African natives have traditionally put part of the honeycomb at the bird's disposal, so ensuring its cooperation in the future.

Most of the birds we have described are specialists, concentrating on a limited range of food for which their bills are specially adapted. For many birds this is obviously an efficient strategy, but others are what we might call jack-of-all-trades, showing little preference for any particular diet. Such birds are often distinguished by general-purpose bills, capable of handling a wide variety of foods, such as small animals, insects, seeds and berries. Among these are numbered most of the crows, thrushes and starlings.

Birds that scavenge for a living usually have equally catholic tastes. In some such cases, the bill, though originally designed for a particular role, has been put to more varied use in the course of time. Thus Herring Gulls, whose staple diet was once probably fish and other marine food, have recently added to their diet by taking food supplied unwittingly by man. Where once their scavenging habits were confined to carrion on the seashore, they are now a familiar sight at fish docks, rubbish tips, and sewerage outlets. Others, like the Black-headed Gull, can scarcely be called seagulls any more, roving far inland in search of worms exposed by the plough, or even the morsels at picnic sites.

In a sense, food is served up on a plate for such species, and their special skill is in quickly recognizing the opportunities offered by novel situations. Here, the Blue Tit excels as an opportunist. One or a few individuals must have discovered the possibility of breaking open milk bottle tops to reveal an easy breakfast, and in England the habit is now widespread.

Some species turn not to man as a source of ready-made food, but to other birds, which they rob of their hard-earned meals. Among the most notorious of such food parasites are the skuas and frigatebirds, which ruthlessly harry other seabirds, forcing them to disgorge the fish they have caught. The risk of suffering injury or even death is usually sufficient incentive to surrender food to these pirates, which are armed with sabre-sharp bills.

Many land birds form flocks, sometimes of enormous size and comprising several different species, which roam the countryside in search of areas of food. In these mixed flocks some advantage may be taken of other species' activities. Flycatching species may seize prey flushed by ground or foliage searching species, and stronger species (like the Great Tit in mixed tit parties in Britain) may rob weaker species of their spoils.

Migration

Most animals have only a limited ability to escape from their immediate surroundings when faced with hardship, and are therefore forced to lead a relatively sedentary life in places where they can survive throughout the year. So persuasive was this belief to many early naturalists, that for a long time they misinterpreted the seasonal comings and goings of many birds, assuming that since they disappeared in the autumn and reappeared in the spring they must be hibernating for the winter. Writing in April 1793, Gilbert White, the famous English naturalist and probably the most astute observer of his time, said of the arrival of Sand Martins: 'The late severe weather considered, it is not very probable that these birds should have migrated so early from a tropical region, through all these cutting winds and pinching frosts: but it is easy to suppose that they, like bats and flies, have been awakened by the influence of the sun, amidst their secret latebrae, where they have spent the uncomfortable foodless months in a torpid state, and the profoundest of slumbers.'

We can scarcely blame Gilbert White for failing to unravel this apparent mystery. It is only since man has been able to travel as widely as the birds themselves that the true nature and scale of migration has been appreciated. We now know that about half the world's birds migrate to some extent. Most have two distinct home ranges, one for breeding and the other wintering. Migration is thus the seasonal movement of the population from one area to the other, usually involving the birds in two journeys each year.

As we might expect, most migrants travel on the wing, which combines the benefits of speed and safety. However, there are some notable exceptions. In the Antarctic spring, Adélie Penguins swim for prodigious distances to reach the mainland from their winter quarters in the pack ice. Once on land, they may still have to journey several miles to their breeding grounds, so they travel partly on foot, partly toboggan-style on their stomachs along the snow, propel-

ling themselves at great speed with their flippers and feet. The American Coot has also been known to migrate on foot, moving *en masse* along the edges of lakes and streams. Divers and auks often swim long distances after vacating their breeding quarters; in the north of Scotland, for instance, Razorbills set out with their young to traverse the North Sea, swimming to their wintering grounds off the Scandinavian coast.

By flight and other means, migration has therefore been widely adopted by a great variety of birds as a means of seeking at a distance whatever they lack at a given time and place. Only where the food supply is sufficiently stable and dependable throughout the year is there little need to move at all. This is especially true of tropical rain forests, where detectable movements are confined largely to the wanderings of species which feed on nectar and fruit. By contrast, tropical savannah birds display definite migrations in response to the seasonal shifts of the rain belts, and the associated flushes of food which favour breeding. In Africa, Quelea and some of the sunbirds make extensive movements north and south with the rains, and thereby avoid the worst of the dry season which follows in their wake. By so doing, they apparently manage to breed in several different areas in the course of a year. Some, like the Carmine Bee-eater, never migrate across the African equator, whereas others, like the White-bellied Stork and the Pennant-winged Nightjar, range far on either side of it to exploit the rain belts of both hemispheres.

It is at higher latitudes, however, that the migratory habit is best developed, since these regions undergo the most striking seasonal fluctuations in food supply. After the cold, barren days of winter, temperatures begin to rise in the spring, triggering off a superabundance of plant and animal life, especially insects, small mammals, plankton and fish. As spring passes into summer, there is the added bonus that nights become progressively shorter, so there are more daylight hours avail-

RIGHT Indian Barheaded Geese *(Anser indica)* annually migrate across the Himalayas, and so hold the altitude record for flying birds.

ABOVE The Wheatear
(Oenanthe oenanthe)
undertakes spectacular
long-distance migrations
from its breeding grounds
in Eurasia and North
America to its wintering
grounds in Africa.

BELOW Part of a huge
soaring flock of migrating
White Storks (Ciconia
ciconia) of the sort that
converges at narrow sea
crossings.

able for collecting food. This state of surplus lasts only a few months, but it is long enough for a huge floating population of summer migrants to raise their young, and move elsewhere before winter sets in again.

Such conditions prevail in both the northern and southern summers, and both exert a powerful influence on migration patterns. The northern hemisphere, however, is especially attractive to birds, since it contains the bulk of the world's land mass. Thus it represents the greatest focal point for migratory land birds. Excluding seabirds, about 589 species breed in Europe and Asia, of which about 40 per cent leave for the winter. Most of the summer visitors to Europe travel south to Africa in the autumn, whereas further east migrants tend to overwinter in either India, South-east Asia or Australasia. The third major migration system is found in the New World, where most migrants commute between North America in the breeding season, and the southern United States, Central or South America in the off-season. The scale of migration in each of these three great pathways is enormous, and in Europe alone at least 1000 million birds are estimated to leave for Africa each autumn.

While the prevailing axis of movement is therefore north-south, there are notable exceptions. When the grip of winter locks up food supplies in the lakes and estuaries of western Siberia, many waders and geese travel almost due west to Britain and Ireland, where the warming Gulf Stream keeps the shores free from ice. Similarly, North American Red-headed Ducks escape from the frozen prairies by travelling east to the Atlantic coast of the United States. In Russia, one species, the Capercaillie, may even migrate north in the winter. It breeds in deciduous woodland but, by contrast, in the autumn, it seeks out evergreen forest where it can browse on the buds and needles of conifers.

For a long time we knew very little about the fate of summer visitors when they disappeared for the winter. What route did they follow, and

how far did they go? How quickly did they get there, and how many of them survived the journey? To answer questions like these, many birds are now marked individually with a light metal ring or band on the leg, engraved with a unique number. With large-scale ringing, it became possible to locate individuals on migration, either by finding them when dead, or by intercepting them *en route* and releasing them again. In addition, a great deal has been learned by direct observation of birds on passage, and more recently by tracking them on radar. By piecing together all this information, a real understanding of migration patterns has emerged in the last few decades.

The routes taken by many migrants are now quite well known. One of the first birds to be studied in detail was the White Stork, whose spring arrival in Europe has long been cause for traditional celebration. In August, after the young are independent, the storks abandon their breeding grounds and embark on a lengthy migration to various destinations in Africa. Like many other large birds, they avoid crossing large stretches of open water, since this would deprive them of the thermals necessary to assist their soaring flight. The White Stork has therefore opted for two routes to get round the obstacles presented by the Black Sea and the Mediterranean. The particular route taken by an individual is dictated by where it was born. Those raised in western Europe traditionally cross the western end of the Mediterranean by the narrow straits of Gibraltar, and then fan out into tropical west Africa. The eastern European birds, on the other hand, cross the Black Sea by the Bosphorus, then skirt the eastern end of the Mediterranean and cross into Africa by way of Suez. Thereafter, they work their way down the east coast of Africa, and may penetrate as far as the southern tip of the continent, thus completing a journey of around 5000 miles (8000 km).

The White Stork was also one of the first species to yield one of the more remarkable facts of migration. A number of storks were raised in captivity, and then released after the rest of the wild population had already departed for Africa. Unable to follow their elders, these naive birds nevertheless selected the correct route, and successfully reached their winter quarters. Experiments like this have provided conclusive evidence that where to fly, and when to stop flying, is often a matter of instinct, but beyond saying that, we have little understanding of how this instinct actually works.

The narrow straits used by White Storks to avoid placing themselves at the full mercy of the sea are also regular focal points for migrants of many other species. During peak migration movements, great numbers of storks, cranes, and various birds of prey converge daily on these corridors. They also channel the migrations of much smaller birds, many of which could not be further removed from the sea in their everyday lives. One day, for instance, I counted 350 Great Spotted Woodpeckers (not a regular migrant, although large numbers of the northern race do erupt from their homeland in

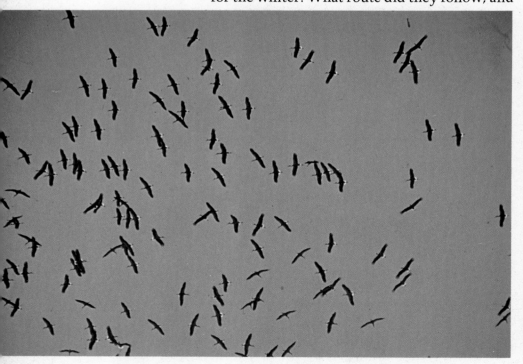

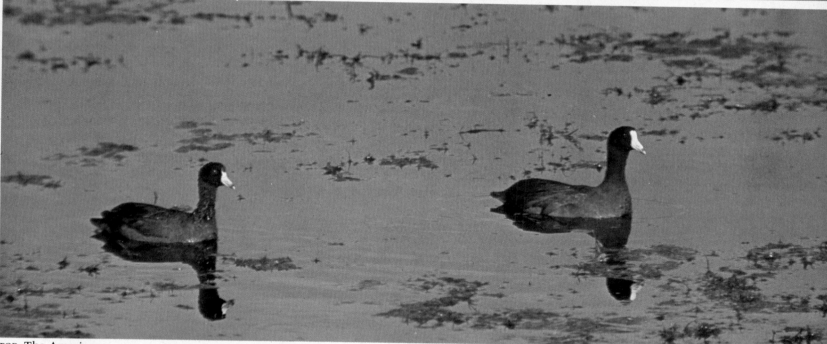

TOP The American Redhead (or Red-headed) Duck *(Aythya americana)*, noted for its east-west migration from the prairies in the summer to the Atlantic coast in the winter.

ABOVE The American Coot *(Fulica americana)* is known to migrate on foot in large numbers.

certain years) hesitantly embarking from the southernmost tip of Sweden, where the Baltic Sea narrows to offer the least hazardous crossing to Germany. Many North American migrants are much more fortunate, since they have no wide seas to negotiate, save the Great Lakes.

East-west mountain ranges present yet another obstacle to European and Asian migrants, and not surprisingly, the birds again opt for the path of least resistance, routing themselves through traditional mountain passes. Again, mountains pose less of a problem for north-south migrants in North America, since the main chains run longitudinally, and may even assist birds to navigate by acting as guidelines.

Many birds, however, migrate at such a height that mountain ranges can be crossed with apparent ease. It is common for migrants to travel at 3000–5000 feet (900–1500 metres) above ground, and sometimes considerably higher. Ducks and geese travelling between

Siberia and India regularly fly at more than 26,000 feet (8000 metres) over the Himalayas, and the record is held by Indian Bar-headed Geese which have been seen at almost 30,000 feet (9000 metres). Considering the special aids needed by man to survive at these altitudes, it is still a great puzzle how birds manage to perform this remarkable feat.

Of the migrants that breed in north temperate latitudes, the most numerous are the insect-eaters – the warblers, flycatchers, wheatears, wagtails and many more. For most of these birds a timely exodus at the end of the summer is essential, since the onset of colder weather spells the sudden disappearance of their prey. Since different birds feed on particular kinds of insects, we find that each times its migration to coincide with the build-up and decline of its preferred prey species. Even closely related species may arrive and depart at different times. In Britain, for example, there is a gradual invasion of the aerial insect-eaters in spring, as successive waves of the various species arrive

ABOVE Swallows and martins assembled on a tree before embarking on migration.

jected to more rigorous winters than others, and stand to gain more from evacuating their breeding grounds. In Europe, for example, northern populations of many species migrate south or south-west for the winter, while more southerly populations remain. These partial migrants include tits, Robins, Blackbirds, Song Thrushes, Starlings, Rooks, Lapwings, and Grey Herons. Thus in Britain where winters are relatively mild, most individuals of these species are resident throughout the year, but during the winter they are joined by a huge influx of their relatives escaping from mainland Europe.

Partial migration is also a widespread phenomenon in North America. Different populations of the American Robin, which breeds from the Canadian tree-line to southern Mexico, vary greatly in their response to the onset of winter. Some remain as far north as British Columbia, but many more move south, and wintering flocks of up to 50,000 birds have been recorded in Florida.

Sex and age also have a strong influence on the tendency to undertake migration. In general, females and young birds leave earliest and travel furthest. This is probably because both are lower in the pecking order than adult males, and so may profit by foregoing competition with them in the testing conditions of winter. In Scandinavia, most female Chaffinches retreat south for the winter, leaving their mates behind to roam the countryside in flocks. The winter surplus of males was known to Linnaeus, the famous Swedish taxonomist, who immortalized the fact when he named the Chaffinch as *Fringilla coelebs* meaning bachelor. In North America, female Song Sparrows and mockingbirds likewise migrate more readily than the males, although the reverse is true of the Ruby-throated Hummingbird; in this instance the males take no part in rearing the young and are free to depart south while their mates are still otherwise engaged.

The tendency of young birds to outdistance their elders is widespread and not confined to land birds. In winter, young Gannets from Europe penetrate south into the Atlantic as far as tropical West Africa, but most adults go no further than the coasts of France and Portugal, as if reluctant to stray very far from the breeding colonies to which, in spring, they will have to return and reassert ownership of hard-earned nest territories.

It is clear from these examples that the distances travelled by different migrants vary considerably from a few hundred to several thousand miles. Body size is evidently no object to long distance travel, and some of the smallest species rank among the most widely travelled of all birds. For example, the Wheatears that breed in the Alaskan tundra ignore the lure of South America, and choose instead to strike westwards across the Bering Straits into Siberia. From there, they traverse most of Asia before veering south towards their final destination in the plains of tropical Africa.

Apparently perverse detours of this kind give us some insight into the likely origins of

to breed at fortnightly intervals. Generally the earliest to appear are the first arrivals of the Sand Martins that so astonished Gilbert White, then the Swallow, and finally the House Martin and Swift. At the end of the summer they depart for Africa in the same order, except for the Swift which leaves a full month ahead of the Sand Martin.

Even within a species we find marked variations in arrival times at different parts of its range. This is because the abundance of insects is strongly dependent on temperature, and the migrants can only advance northwards as fast as the weather improves their food supply. Because spring is later to arrive in eastern than western Europe, Swallows are already in England when further east they are still 300 miles (480 km) further south at the northern shores of the Black Sea.

Within a species, we often find that some populations are migratory while others are not. This may arise if a species occupies a wide range of latitude, so that some individuals are sub-

migration itself. During the last ice age, vast areas of the northern hemisphere were effectively as barren as the polar ice caps, imprisoning bird populations south of the glaciated belt. As the ice gradually retreated to expose the land surface again, many birds must have extended their breeding range northwards by invading these hitherto hostile regions, although they would have had to return south again for the winter. It is probable that the ancestral breeding range of Wheatears was thus confined to southern Europe and Asia, which is still their stronghold today. From this early stock, we can imagine pioneering Wheatears spreading eastwards with the retreat of the ice, and eventually blazing a trail to Alaska. The dog-leg route of the modern Alaskan migrants may therefore be in keeping with long-established tradition.

No less renowned as an extraordinary traveller is the little Arctic Warbler. Its breeding range is similar to the Wheatear's, extending across the birch and coniferous forests of Asia from Scandinavia to western Alaska. Most of these birds must cover about 8000 miles (12,800 km) twice a year in their journeys to and from wintering grounds in tropical south-east Asia. Among small American birds that have established winter quarters in South America, one of the furthest travelled is the Bobolink, an icterid of about starling size, which breeds in marshy habitats in Canada and the northern United States. In the autumn, it travels in large flocks along a well-defined migration route to

Florida, and from there it proceeds by a series of island hops through Cuba and Jamaica, finally crossing the Caribbean to Brazil and penetrating as far south as northern Argentina. Some 6200 miles (10,000 km) span the gap between the extremities of the Bobolink's total range.

The most astonishing feature of all these long-distance migrations is that they involve hazardous sea crossings, and these, moreover, have to be accomplished in a single non-stop flight. The Wheatears which breed in Greenland launch themselves across the Atlantic in the autumn, and do not sight land till they reach northern Spain over 2000 miles (3000 km) away. Similarly, the Arctic Warbler commits itself to a long oceanic flight from Asia, before it makes a landfall on the island archipelagos of the South Pacific, where it overwinters.

Even more remarkable feats of endurance and navigation are demanded when the migrant's destination consists of only a relatively small, isolated island surrounded by trackless ocean wastes. Such is the achievement of the Pacific race of the Golden Plover, which makes an uninterrupted flight from western Alaska to Hawaii, a minimum journey of over 2000 miles (3000 km). Similarly, the Bristle-thighed Curlew somehow manages to steer an accurate course across the Pacific from the Canadian Arctic to Tahiti, an even smaller target than Hawaii. Comparable journeys are made by two species of cuckoo that breed in New Zealand. The Long-tailed Cuckoo sets off northwards to

ABOVE In Scandinavia, the Chaffinch (Fringilla coelebs) is a partial migrant, the females migrating south into Europe for the winter while the males (shown here) stay behind.

BELOW The Bobolink (Dolichonyx oryzivorus) is one of the best known and furthest travelled American migrants.

seek out its winter quarters in the Pacific islands strung out between New Guinea and the Marquesas, while the Shining Cuckoo heads for the Solomons and the Bismarck Archipelago. The adult birds depart early, while their off-spring are still being tended by foster-parents, so the young cuckoos make the journey quite independently, without any directional clues from their parents.

None of these birds have any opportunity to feed *en route*, so we may well ask how they manage to perform such marathon journeys without running out of energy and dropping into the sea. The answer lies in the enormous fat reserves which the birds lay down as high-energy fuel before they set off. The smaller the bird is, the relatively larger are the fat reserves it has to accumulate; the tiny Ruby-throated Hummingbird weighs only about one-tenth of an ounce (2.5–2.8 grams), but it almost doubles its weight with fat before migrating the 500 miles (800 km) across the Gulf of Mexico from the coast of Florida to the Yucatan Peninsula.

This fuel reserve leaves the bird a little in hand to allow for the hindrance of unexpected head-winds, but for safety's sake it still has to make the non-stop flight inside 24 hours. Fat is there-fore an essential lifeline wherever small birds have to traverse barren regions, whether they be sea, deserts, or mountain ranges. Many warblers migrating south from Europe resign themselves to fasting on an unbroken flight of 1200 miles (1920 km) across the Mediterranean Sea and the Sahara Desert. This journey must take a warbler at least 48 hours and often longer, so budgeting its fuel reserves accurately in advance is vitally important.

Seabirds on migration are obviously under much less pressure than land birds, since they can replenish themselves along the way. They therefore have the potential to circumnavigate the entire globe and some, like the Wandering Albatross, do just this. The record distance travelled by any bird, land or sea, between its breeding and winter quarters, is held by the Arctic Tern. Many of them breed north of the

Arctic circle and migrate to Antarctic waters for the northern winter, a journey of at least 8000 miles (12,800 km) each way. The birds encounter a succession of different wind belts as they proceed, and their migration routes are deflected accordingly, so that the round trip must involve some individuals in a journey of about 22,000 miles (35,000 km). To have evolved at all, the advantages of ranging so far must be enormous, and it is significant that the Arctic Tern's annual migration enables it to experience both the Arctic and Antarctic summers of 24 hours daylight, and so gives it the best of both worlds as far as feeding conditions are concerned.

Lengthy trans-equatorial migrations are also performed by other seabirds, notably the Short-tailed Shearwater or Muttonbird, which annually makes a grand tour of the Pacific Ocean. Abandoning their breeding grounds in south-east Australasia and Tasmania, the birds first head northwards and then veer west to skirt the coast of Japan. From there, they describe a clockwise path, sweeping round the Bering Sea in the height of the rich, northern summer, and then down the west coast of America, before turning westwards to cross their original outward path in the region of the tropics. Then it is a relatively short haul down the east coast of Australia to return them to their starting point. Like the Arctic Tern, the shearwaters' strategy behind their great looping route is to avail themselves of geographical and seasonal differences in the direction of tailwinds. The scale of the shearwaters' migration is epic in every sense. The round trip involves over 20,000 miles (32,000 km) of flying, and for five months the birds are entirely dependent on what the Pacific Ocean can provide in the way of food and a place to sleep. In days gone by, the numbers of migrating shearwaters used to be vast, and one ship's report records the passage of an estimated 150 million birds, which had been sighted travelling together in one huge flock.

Probably the most enduring riddle about migration is how birds manage to navigate themselves successfully over such long distances. As we have seen, survival itself depends on an unerring precision, especially for small land birds which have no latitude for route-finding by trial and error. Apart from the familiar homing abilities of pigeons, a number of examples from wild birds will serve to show that navigation is anything but a haphazard process. A Manx Shearwater was taken from its breeding burrow on the Welsh island of Skokholm, transported across the Atlantic, and released at Boston airport. It was back on its nest only twelve and a half days later, so that it averaged almost 250 miles (400 km) a day on its return flight. The Shearwater must therefore have known where Boston was located relative to Skokholm on the map, and seems to have made a beeline for home. Bird-ringing has also helped to reveal how fast some birds travel on migration. Few cases of high-speed travel are likely to better that of the Knot (a small wading bird), ringed in the British Isles, and subsequently recovered only eight days later in Liberia, 3500 miles (5600 km) away.

It is now becoming clear that most migrants probably have a wide variety of route-finding methods at their disposal. The earliest theories sought to explain navigation in terms of plotting the sun's position. A great deal of evidence has accumulated to uphold this idea, although there is still considerable controversy over practicalities. Many migrants, however, travel by night as well; indeed land birds which make non-stop flights across seas and deserts have no alternative but to battle on after nightfall, since there is nowhere they can stop to feed or rest. Moreover, some migrants appear to travel exclusively at night, especially the waders, ducks, tyrant-flycatchers, most thrushes, and warblers. This suggested that the night sky, too, might be used for orientation, and a number of experiments support this view.

Mallards, displaced from home and released at night, immediately take up the right direction if the sky is clear, but if overcast, they

FAR LEFT The range of many Arctic Terns (Sterna paradisaea) extends from north of the Arctic circle to the Antarctic, making them the most celebrated of all long-distance migrants.

LEFT Experiments with the Manx Shearwater (Puffinus puffinus) which breeds on the west coast of Britain and winters off the Brazilian coast, have demonstrated its unerring homing ability.

disperse in random directions, apparently
totally disorientated. The birds' chief source of
information seems to come from the so-called
fixed stars such as the Pole Star, although conclusive proof of this was lacking before the
advent of the artificial night sky provided by
the man-made planetarium. Captive Blackcaps
and Lesser Whitethroats were placed in a
planetarium in spring, when their normal direction of migration was reflected in the movements they made inside their cage. Remarkably, it was found that the birds' direction of
movement could be altered at will by suitable
adjustment of key constellations. Under a
spring sky, they correctly orientated themselves north-eastwards, but when presented
with a replica of the autumn sky, they altered
course to head south-west, in keeping with
their normal migratory habits at that time of
year.

Thus, both the sun and the stars are used by
migrants for path-finding and, moreover,
adjustment is made for seasonal differences in
star patterns. Recently it has been shown that
birds are also able to sense variations in the
earth's magnetic field, although it remains to
be demonstrated whether this actually assists
in navigation. In addition to these subtle clues,
birds can learn much from an intimate knowledge of the terrain along their migration route.
Mountain ranges, valleys, river systems, lakes,
coastline and other conspicuous landmarks undoubtedly help to provide the fine adjustment
of flight paths. The northward movement of
swallows and seabirds mentioned earlier also
illustrates a widespread sensitivity to weather
patterns. Prevailing winds offer a reliable
source of information on a bird's whereabouts,
and it has also been shown that pigeons are
responsive to changes in atmospheric pressure.

Thus birds appear to have several different
aids for plotting their position, and most migrants probably use all of them to some extent.
Different species and populations must somehow be able to trace their particular migration
route by inheriting the exact set of compass
bearings needed to define it. This is not to say
that every bird is perfectly programmed at
birth to accomplish the perfect migration.
Learning certainly plays a part, and we know
that orientation improves with age and experience.

Despite recent advances in our understanding of migration, a great many questions obviously remain to be answered. To explain how a
bird knows where to migrate by saying that it
has an inbuilt blueprint of the journey merely
buries the real answer a little deeper.

Courtship and Display

The approach of the breeding season is a period of radical change among birds, particularly for the males, which usually take the initiative in wooing a mate and finding a suitable place to raise a family. It is a time of intense rivalry, when birds have to appear as attractive as possible to members of the opposite sex, and as formidable as they can to those of the same sex. Under the powerful influence of the sex hormones, startling alterations in appearance and behaviour equip birds for the rivalry of courtship and display. Many change into a colourful new breeding dress and some grow lavish ornamental plumes. In many species, the male is suddenly transformed into a virtuoso songster, and he acquires the ability to perform extraordinary aerobatic and gymnastic feats. So, he becomes the embodiment of his claim to be a desirable husband and an able parent.

His first task is often to obtain a breeding territory, which may be quite a substantial area, containing in some cases all the food the pair will need to keep themselves and raise a brood. Sometimes, however, birds cannot nest in the midst of their food supply, and in such cases the territory may be little larger than the nest itself. This is true of many colonial sea-birds, like the Guillemot, which lays claim to only a few square inches of cliff ledge amongst its neighbours. Here, the territory appears to serve merely as a place to which the male can attract a mate, and where the pair can subsequently breed in peace. Between these two extremes of territory size, we find numerous intermediate situations, where the pair feeds partly inside its territory and partly outside.

There are usually more males than territories available, so fierce competition reigns for the available space at the beginning of the breeding season. Various threat displays are used by males to contest territorial rights, and by the winner to advertize the location and boundaries of his claim. The rivalry is particularly intense between males in immediately adjacent territories, and physical battles do occur, although for relatively short periods. Symbolic threat displays probably evolved as a substitute for real fighting, which can injure both parties.

When two rivals confront each other in a border dispute, they try to look as intimidating as possible by increasing their apparent size and exposing conspicuous patterns and colours. The European Robin responds aggressively to any other male encroaching on his territory, by turning front on to the opponent and puffing out his red breast feathers to display the maximum area of colour. So provocative is this signal that the male Robin may even attack a bundle of red feathers.

This automatic reaction poses a real problem in courtship, since male and female Robins look alike. A female attracted into the territory is attacked at first just as if she was a male. This is likely to happen in any species where the sexes look alike, such as grebes, gulls and tits. The Robin illustrates the general rule that displays mounted to repel rival males also serve to attract females.

While plumage and postures are useful de-

RIGHT The spectacular courtship display of the Argus Pheasant (Argusianus argus), a native of Malaya, Sumatra and Borneo.

BELOW LEFT The sight of the red breast feathers in an 'intruding' stuffed Robin (Erithacus rubecula) elicits a fierce attack from the territory-owning male.

vices for threatening rivals at close quarters, the male would obviously forestall endless territorial disputes if he could proclaim his presence to distant rivals. Such a proclamation would have the added advantage of attracting passing females into his territory. Many birds have therefore evolved a long-range display, and the form it takes is strongly influenced by the sort of habitat the bird occupies.

Woodland birds communicate with each other largely by song, since visual signals would be hard to detect. In fact many of the best singers are noted for their camouflage colouring, and lack any plumage patterns that could be used for display. The male usually has a number of strategically placed song posts inside his territory, and in the course of the day he usually broadcasts from all of these. Vocal duets with neighbours are especially frequent and intense at the beginning of the breeding season, when territorial boundaries are still fluid and mates still in demand. Male Pied Flycatchers, for example, are known to sing 3600 times a day before obtaining a mate and only 1000 times a day afterwards. Red-eyed Vireos are even more indefatigable performers, and sing on average 22,000 times a day at the peak of their vocal activity.

In part, the decline in singing as the breeding season proceeds reflects the growing familiarity between neighbouring territory owners. An individual's song is unique and recognizable as such to its rivals. After a few weeks of vocal confrontation, hostility gives way to a certain mutual respect between neighbours. The volume of song therefore subsides when its message becomes superfluous. This truce is valuable since it releases the males for parental duties, not least finding food for their offspring.

In species like the American Robin, Mockingbird and White-crowned Sparrow, song is no longer confined to the male. Sometimes, as in the European Robin, both sexes hold temporary territories in the autumn, and then both the female and the male sing. However, there are a few families such as the jacanas, phalaropes, painted snipe, button quails, and tinamous in which the females take all the initiative in courtship and display, as does the Dotterel, unlike most of its relatives in the plover family.

Where both sexes sing, this may contribute to establishing a bond between the pair and cementing their relationship. A true dialogue sometimes develops between them, though most commonly it occurs as a disorderly succession of calls and answers, with frequent interruptions of one by the other. The cacophony of noise in many large seabird colonies obscures a multitude of intimate conversations of this kind.

The most sophisticated dialogues are undoubtedly the song duets characteristic of a number of tropical land birds. In most instances, the two members of a pair sing in unison. The song duets of several species of ovenbirds, antbirds and motmots of Central and South America have been described. Even more remarkable are the performances of some of the South American tyrant-flycatchers, Central

American wrens, African shrikes, barbets, and grass-warblers, in which the mates do not sing together but one after the other, alternating with such precise timing that the notes appear to issue from a single bird. The two birds do not always sing the same phrase; for example, in the Blackheaded Gonolek, an African shrike, the first bird utters a *yoik* call, and the second bird follows immediately with a rending, hiss-like sound.

One final peculiarity of bird-song which has never been satisfactorily explained is the habit of mimicking the calls and songs of other species. Many birds can do this to some extent, and in Britain alone about thirty species are credited with some ability for it. A few mimics, however, are renowned for their exceptional versatility and uncanny accuracy. Among these are ranked the cosmopolitan Starling, the African robin chats, and the Australian lyrebirds, bowerbirds, and scrub birds. Though we tend to rate most highly as mimics those captive birds like the parrots and mynahs that can learn human speech, many wild birds have repertoires of birdsong that are no less phenomenal. For instance, the North American Mockingbird, so called for its habit of aping bird-calls, has been known to imitate as many as 55 other species in under an hour.

Whether or not mimicry helps in territorial defence and pair formation is a moot point, but one possible clue to its function is that some of the best mimics live in dense scrub where recognition by sound is most important. In this habitat mimicry may help to distinguish the individual from its neighbours with other song patterns.

Some birds also proclaim their presence by non-vocal sounds. Among woodland species, the best-known are the woodpeckers, which hammer their bills rhythmically against hollow trees to produce drum rolls that carry great distances. Both sexes join in this territorial display, producing sounds characteristic of their own species. Like song, drumming is especially intense at the start of the breeding season; Great Spotted Woodpeckers, for example, drum up to 500–600 times a day during the peak period of display.

Some birds of open country employ non-vocal sounds of a different sort to draw attention to their nuptial flights. In snipe, the specially stiffened outer tail feathers are fanned out when the bird dives earthwards, so that they vibrate with a drumming or bubbling sound, not unlike the noise of liquid pouring jerkily out of a bottle. Similarly, the specialized tail feathers of the Paradise Whydah produce an unmistakable buzzing sound during its display flights.

Most birds of open ground, however, rely as much on being seen as heard, using a combination of colour and movement to advertize themselves. Usually the focus of display is the plumage, though this is not always the case. Some of the most captivating attractions are provided by areas of brilliantly coloured skin. In the breeding season, male frigatebirds can inflate a vivid crimson throat pouch, so that it

bulges like a grotesque balloon. Crouching on his chosen nest site in a tree or bush, the male distends this sac, quivers his outspread wings, and rattles his bill, thereby hoping to catch the attention of a female flying overhead.

Somewhat less frantic is the endearing nuptial display of the Blue-footed Booby, which inhabits the Pacific coasts between Mexico and Peru. As the name suggests, this species is distinguished by the azure-blue colour of its legs and webbed feet. It shows off this handsome feature to best advantage by goose-stepping slowly round its mate with the webs fully extended.

In albatrosses, the pair join in a courtship dance of great beauty. The sequence usually begins with the birds facing each other and bowing repeatedly. As the ritual reaches a crescendo, both birds begin to move in a circle with their enormous wings outspread and their bills pointed skywards, to the accompaniment of resounding cries. As the excitement subsides, the wings are folded and each bird clatters its bill against the other's like two swordsmen fencing. Finally, the ceremony ends as it started with the pair bowing sedately in mutual acknowledgment. A ritualized display of this kind is clearly directed more at the partner than at any potential usurper. Above all, it seems to be a gesture of mutual confidence, and so helps to foster the bond between the already-mated pair. Such rituals are often acted out as a greeting ceremony, when one member of a pair arrives back on the territory after an absence to join its mate.

Unlike the display of frigatebirds, in which the garish male does all the posturing to his plainer mate, the most striking feature of the albatrosses' display is that both sexes play an equal part. This is made possible because both sexes are alike, and neither is privileged with more striking looks than the other. Similarly the male and female boobies are both endowed with the all-important blue feet, so again neither sex is relegated to a passive role in courtship. Sexual equality is particularly evident in the penguins and their intimate nuptial dances. Paired Adélie Penguins stand face to face and, with bills pointed skywards, each commences to sway its head from left to right, but out of phase with its partner. At the same time, the birds rock gently back and forth, uttering a deep-throated *ka-ka*.

Like most colonial seabirds, however, such open affection is strictly confined to the nest site. Penguins nest on the ground in dense rookeries, often numbering thousands of birds. Since they cannot fly, they have to reach their nests on foot. To do so, they are forced to run the gauntlet of all the territory owners blocking their path, and squabbles are frequent. The Adélie Penguin is one of the most aggressive of its kind, and its colonies are invariably in uproar, with every bird constantly vigilant lest its nest be trampled on.

The constraint of a small nesting territory sandwiched amongst others has presumably contributed to the evolution of intricate, localized displays like the Adélie Penguin's. Where territories are larger, greater freedom of movement is possible, and behaviour can be less stereotyped. The ultimate in energetic displays are undoubtedly those performed in the air. As these are highly conspicuous, they serve both to impress potential mates and repel rival males. One of the best loved aerial displays in spring is the soaring, melodious flight of the Skylark. Sharing the same meadow might be Lapwings, which alternately swoop and soar with great abandon, rolling from side to side to flash their broad black-and-white wings, and all the time uttering their piercing, liquid cries. Even more dizzying are the aerobatic manoeuvres of certain birds of prey, such as buzzards and harriers. Sometimes, one bird will climb skywards and then descend towards its mate which, with split-second timing, turns over in mid-air and stretches out its talons to grapple momentarily with those of its partner.

In many aerial displays, special adornments are brought to the fore. As they twist and turn after each other along a cliff face, courting

ABOVE In the Blue-crowned Motmot (*Momotus momota*) the racquet-shaped tips of the tail are highlighted in display.

CENTRE LEFT A Common Tern (*Sterna hirundo*) offers his mate a fish, helping both to nourish her prior to egg-laying and cement the pair bond.

BELOW LEFT 'Sky-pointing' in the courtship display of the Adélie Penguin (*Pygoscelis adeliae*) in which both sexes play an active part.

tropic-birds show off their long, whip-like tail streamers which wave up and down in flight. Bishop birds and widow-birds likewise fly back and forth over their grassland territories, displaying their long tail plumes or their black-and-red plumage. Male Jackson's Widow-birds draw even more explicit attention to their wafting tails, by bouncing up and down like yo-yos on their display grounds. In courtship flight, the male hummingbird tantalizes the duller female by executing mercurial changes of direction, now exposing his dazzling patches of iridescent colour, now taunting her by turning to withhold them from view.

In many cases it is only in display that we can appreciate the full significance of adornments like these, which otherwise may strike us as useless and sometimes even a hindrance to their owners. So it is with the racquet-shaped tails of the tropical American motmots. Each of the two central tail feathers has a long wire-like shaft ending in a leaf-like vane, so that together they resemble a pair of delicate spoons. Mot-

mots are thus equipped for a kind of graceful semaphore signalling between the sexes as they flick, twist, or swing their tails like pendulums.

For some aquatic birds, the water surface presents an ideal stage for elaborate courtship performances. Great-crested Grebes, though clumsy and sluggish on land, are transformed creatures on the water, where they act out a courtship dance renowned for its elegance. Throughout. they seem to adopt a variety of different facial expressions by raising or lowering their handsome double crest and velvety collar. The dance has many phases, but the finale is commonly the celebrated weed ceremony, which begins with the pair swimming apart on the surface and each diving to seek a piece of water weed. If both are successful in their quest, they swim hurriedly back towards each other, carrying the weed in their bills. As they meet, they rear vertically out of the water, breast to breast, and keeping stiffly upright, tread the water furiously with much splashing, all the time shaking their heads briskly from

side to side. Some species are even more frenzied, careering wildly together across the surface in all directions.

Symbolic offerings are frequent in courtship display. In the case of grebes, water weed represents the building material of their nest platform, and presumably signifies shared commitment to the breeding venture. Herons and egrets which build large, twiggy nests likewise present gifts of sticks to their mates. In other species food items are offered instead. A male tit, for example, may feed his mate a great many caterpillars in the course of a day. She actively solicits this food by adopting a submissive, crouching posture, quivering her wings, and calling peevishly. At the start of the breeding season, male terns feed fish to their mates in similar fashion. Courtship feeding was once viewed as no more than a symbolic gesture, but it seems likely to serve a more practical function as well. It probably helps the female to meet the extra energy demands of forming eggs, and may also allow her to gauge how efficient a provider her husband is likely to be later on when there are chicks to be fed.

However, pride of place amongst birds that use objects as visual aids must go to the bizarre courtship antics of the bowerbirds of Australia and New Guinea, so-called for the males' unique habit of building a special nuptial chamber designed to entice a mate. The Satin Bowerbird pushes two upright rows of dry twigs into the ground, so that they arch inwards at the top to form a corridor about a foot (30 cm) high and six inches (fifteen cm) wide. He then proceeds to daub the interior with a paste of crushed blueberries, often using a sliver of bark as a brush. The finishing touches are put by littering the entrance with decorative objects, mostly blue in colour, which he gleans from the neighbourhood, such as feathers, shells, berries, beetles' wing-cases, bottle tops, and other trinkets. His masterpiece complete, the male awaits the arrival of a female curious to inspect his handiwork. When this happens, his anticipation is ill-concealed; he puffs himself out, sings distractedly, and fusses round his bower, periodically picking up and showing off odd treasures from his hoard. If the female approves of what she sees, she may fall for the suitor's advances, and enter the bower, whereupon he rushes in and mates with her. For her part, the female ceases to show much further interest in the bower and seeks a suitable tree nearby, where she alone builds a nest and rears the offspring. Meanwhile, her promiscuous husband is already busy, showing his wares to any other female he might persuade to mate with him.

The design of the bower varies from species to species, but none is more sophisticated than that of the gardener bowerbirds, which erect a central pillar of branches and roof it over with sticks to form a maypole-like structure or a conical hut with doorway. Some also construct a surrounding stockade, and decorate it with brightly coloured flowers and berries. The males continue to maintain the beauty of these buildings from one season to the next, making running repairs as necessary.

No other species has risen to the bowerbirds' constructional art, and instead some resort to using the nest-site itself as a lure for the female. This is especially common where the site gains prestige by being a comparatively rare commodity like a hole in a tree. Once male Pied Flycatchers have discovered a potential nest hole, they defend only a small area around it. The ownership of a suitable hole is the male's prize possession, and he courts any passing female by making a great show of disappearing into his chamber, hoping to entice her in as well.

The nearest equivalent to the bowerbirds are species in which the male selects a suitable patch of ground to flaunt himself in front of females. Usually, this is a simple clearing, devoid of any decoration, and the male relies on his plumage, colouration and vocal talents to attract a mate. Few birds are better endowed in all these respects than the Argus Pheasant, a relative of the peacocks. The crowning glory of the male's plumage is his extraordinary tail and

wings. The central tail feathers are exceptionally long, while the wing feathers are huge and broad at the tips, finely speckled with grey, blue, chestnut and buff, and overlain with prominent eye spots. He takes up stance on his jungle clearing and hoists these vast wings, hiding his head behind them to display a continuous fan-shaped tapestry. With loud, penetrating calls, he attracts females into the vicinity of his spectacular exhibition, and warns off rival males.

In display, the Superb Lyrebird must compete with the Argus Pheasant for sheer flair. The male constructs numerous circular clearings in the forest, each about three feet (one metre) across, and slightly raised. These mounds set the daily scene for a number of bewitching performances. The beautiful tail, comprising two silvery, mauve and gold, lyre-shaped plumes, and several long, delicate filaments, is spread and arched over the head to hang like a lace veil. The bird now begins to dance to the rhythm of a vigorous song, composed partly of

his own notes and partly the mimicked calls of other birds. For all this bravado, the Lyrebird is a shy and secretive bird, confined to eastern Australia, and was unknown to the outside world till 1798.

In a number of other species, the males compete for supremacy on a communal display ground. There is a certain amount of camaraderie, as members of a group defend the arena against strangers. Each male probably benefits in a further sense, since females may be brought to a higher pitch of excitement by the spectacle of a massed display, than by the individual efforts of a solitary male. In short, the attraction of the whole seems to be greater than the sum of its parts. Here, however, the corporate spirit ends, with each male out to demonstrate his absolute superiority over his colleagues, and his exclusive claim to mating rights.

One of the most celebrated communal displays is that of the Black Grouse, which frequents moorland and young conifer plantations in northern Europe. Its assemblies have long

ABOVE A Satin Bowerbird *(Ptilonorhynchus violacea)* attends to his bower, decorating it with feathers and other blue oddments.

77

ripe oranges when fully inflated. In the closely related Sage Grouse, the fully distended sacs droop from the neck like an immense ermine robe, and are periodically deflated with explosive force, sending a loud report booming across the plains. The communal assemblies of the Sage Grouse can be massive in scale, with up to several hundred males congregating on a strip about half a mile long. Like the Black Grouse, the key figures are the dominant males occupying the pole positions in the centre, and the strongest bird may succeed in pairing with twenty or more females in a morning.

The lek displays of the Ruff evoke the atmosphere of a medieval joust. The males are distinguished by a heraldic ruff of feathers, each contestant sporting a different colour from his rivals. In great excitement, they display before the soberly clad females, who judge between the performers and choose a mate.

In all species who perform at a lek, one of the most intriguing questions is why the males can afford to advertize themselves with their noticeable plumage with apparent scant regard for their personal safety, when other birds depend on their plumage for camouflage from predators. By contrast, lekking females are invariably drab. The difference is highlighted by those birds-of-paradise that indulge in elaborate communal displays. Here, the females are as strikingly plain as the males are strikingly exotic. Again, in the lekking Cock-of-the-rock, found in the South American tropics, the male has a brilliant livery of orange or red, topped with a handsome, helmet-like crest, while the female pales in comparison. Male manakins, related to the Cock-of-the-rock, and noted for their gymnastic group displays, also boast much brighter colours than the females.

To trace the probable origins of such contrasts in appearance between the sexes, we have to appreciate the hazards of making a successful nesting attempt. Both ground-nesters, like grouse and the Ruff, and tropical forest birds such as those described above, are particularly vulnerable to predation, so the less attention they attract to the nest site the better. Two birds active around the nest are more conspicuous than one, so lekking species have evolved a division of labour between the sexes, whereby the female undertakes all the domestic duties from nest-building through to brood care, while the male's responsibilities end when he has fertilized her.

This arrangement allows the male to be completely promiscuous, so much so that the Sage Grouse may acquire a sizeable harem in a single morning. Intense competition for the available females will then favour the development of brighter and more eye-catching plumage and ornaments in the males, and the establishment of communal display grounds where they can demonstrate their prowess. For her part, the female will benefit most by adopting a demure, cryptic dress to help protect her from discovery at the nest. The overall strategy is therefore very complex, and it is remarkable that so many different species have arrived at the same devious solution to a common problem.

ABOVE The male Cock-of-the-rock *(Rupicola rupicola)* is brilliantly attired to compete against other males on the communal display grounds.

ABOVE RIGHT In a flock of Black-necked Cranes *(Grus nigricollis)* which inhabit high central Asia, a pair indulge in a leaping courtship dance.

RIGHT Male Sage Grouse *(Centrocercus urophasianus)* compete for females by a combination of sound (from the throat sac), dance, and plumage adornment.

been known as leks from the Swedish *leka*, meaning to play. The males, or Blackcock, gather at a regular daily rendezvous, traditionally patronized over the years by successive generations of the local population. Each male holds a small individual territory and stages mock fights with his neighbours. At first the hens stay in the background, but are soon drawn towards the scene of the battle, whereupon each enters the males' territories one at a time. From this point on, she commands all his attention; he swells his wattles, spreads his wings and lyre-shaped tail, and half-prostrate, proceeds to run circles round her, grunting and gobbling with excitement. The strongest bird may secure most of the matings, subordinate birds doing less well, with males at the bottom of the pecking order winning no favours.

In the case of the North American Prairie Chicken, the spoils are more evenly shared, and probably all the males achieve some success. The courtship display is a full-blooded war dance, as they stomp on the ground with their feet, pounding out an unmistakable drum message to their captive audience. Prairie Chickens are also noted for the remarkable air-sacs flanking the throat, which bulge like two

Nesting and Breeding

Most birds breed in a well-defined period of the year, when food supplies are abundant, since only then can they find enough to meet the extra energy demands of forming eggs and raising a brood. In temperate regions, therefore, birds nest in the summer, although the start of the breeding season and its duration varies between species depending on their particular diet. In Britain, Blackbirds and Song Thrushes are among the first to nest, often laying in March, or exceptionally even February, as soon as the spring rains soften the soil enough to make earthworms more accessible. Many insectivorous birds of woodland, like the tits and Robins, cannot begin till April and May, when caterpillars emerge from the opening buds, while others, like the Spotted Flycatcher, wait for the appearance of flying insects later on. One of the last European species to breed is Eleonora's Falcon, which lays late in the Mediterranean summer, so that its young hatch in time to be fed on the hosts of small birds passing south on autumn migration.

Many birds ensure a food supply for themselves and their offspring by claiming a large enough territory at the start of the breeding season. Since each breeding pair is then separated from its nearest neighbours by the breadth of its territory, such birds are effectively solitary nesters. In contrast, many other species congregate in dense breeding colonies, often numbering thousands or even millions of pairs. Colonial breeding is practised by a variety of landbirds, including herons, swifts and some species of swallows, Rooks, weaver-finches and some birds of prey. However, the habit is most widespread amongst seabirds of all kinds, notably the petrels, gannets, auks, gulls, and terns, which often assemble in huge numbers to breed, sometimes taking over whole islands for the purpose. Each pair breeds in the centre of its own private site, surrounded by countless others. Frequently, the territory barely exceeds the nest in area. North Atlantic Gannets, for example, space themselves about three feet (one metre) apart, while Guillemots are even closer together, nesting shoulder to shoulder on precarious ledges.

Why do some species, and particularly most seabirds, prefer to nest in colonies? From the feeding point of view, there is usually no special advantage to seabirds in solitary nesting, for they cannot position themselves within the area of their food supply as many land birds do. On the positive side, colony members, even among land birds, may benefit one another by revealing the position of localized food patches scattered in the hinterland of their colony. By studying the flight path taken by a bird returning with food, others may be able to follow suit and discover the source for themselves. Shared information of this kind could be particularly valuable in tracking down highly mobile and elusive shoals of fish. A further advantage of group nesting is that predators are less likely to risk the concerted attack of a whole colony. Seabirds, notably terns, will readily band together to dive-bomb and otherwise harass any would-be predator that gets too close.

BELOW LEFT Song Thrush *(Turdus philomelos)* nestlings, like those of other passerines, are naked, blind, and relatively helpless at birth.

RIGHT Common Guillemots *(Uria aalge)* crowd on to narrow cliff ledges to breed.

BOTTOM A Burrowing Owl *(Speotyto cunicularia)* at the entrance to its nest tunnel excavated in the ground.

BELOW The Yellow-billed Tropic-bird *(Phaethon lepturus)* nests in a small rock crevice which it defends fiercely against intruders.

However small and insignificant a seabird's territory may appear, it is as precious to its owner as a patch of lush woodland is to a male Robin. Each has fought for his ground against fierce competition, and only after victory are his prospects of breeding assured. Once a male is the accepted owner of a good territory, therefore, he frequently returns to occupy it in successive breeding seasons. This is true of land birds as well as seabirds, and many holders of large territories are even faithful to a particular nest-site. Eagles and Peregrine Falcons resort year after year to traditional eyries, and some quite small birds are no less tenacious, swallows returning to reclaim the same barn and Pied Flycatchers the same nest hole.

Such a strong bond with a specific territory has much to recommend it. It makes sense to continue breeding in a place that has proved successful in the past. Furthermore, though many birds are known to pair for life, they do not necessarily keep in contact with their mate outside the breeding season. They may, for instance, become separated during long migrations. However, as long as the pair have a permanent territory, they have a familiar meeting ground at the start of each breeding season.

After territories are established and birds pair, the breeding season proceeds to the important task of nest-building. Different species vary enormously both in their choice of nest-site and in the sort of nest they build, ranging from shallow depressions on the ground to elaborate tree-houses. The King and Emperor Penguins make no nest. As soon as the female Emperor lays her single egg in the Antarctic autumn, she entrusts it to the care of the male, while she sets off for the sea, often 40–60 miles (64–96 km) away, to fatten up in readiness for the harsh winter days ahead. Meanwhile, the male balances the egg on top of his feet and envelops it beneath a warming fold of abdominal skin. He continues to incubate stoically like this for the nine weeks it takes to hatch, whereupon the female returns and takes over brooding the chick, cradling it in the same fashion as the egg.

Not making even a semblance of a nest, Emperor Penguins are not restricted to a nest-site. The egg or chick is almost as much part of its parent as a baby kangaroo, and the adults are free to shuffle about, taking their nest and its contents with them. Clearly, the Emperor Penguins have evolved this unique behaviour to cope with the exceptionally hostile conditions of the Antarctic interior. Elsewhere, in more hospitable environments, other penguins retain fixed nest-sites, though sometimes there is little to distinguish the nest from its surroundings; Adélie and Chinstrap Penguins gather together only a few small stones around a scrape on the bare ground. Humboldt Penguins, however, seek the added protection of the sea caves along the Chilean and Peruvian coasts where they congregate to breed.

Several other species of seabirds also build rudimentary nests or slight scrapes in rock crevices, notably the tropic-birds and various auks, such as the Little Auk, Black Guillemot, and Razorbill. If the recess is a shallow one, open to view, the sitting birds usually face the entrance ready to confront any intruder. Tropic-birds and Razorbills are especially menacing in this respect, deterring all but the most resolute predator by lunging forward with their sharp, powerful bills.

Many land birds also nest on bare ground, sometimes using no more than a shallow scrape devoid of any lining material. The Ostrich makes a nest of this kind, in which fifteen to twenty eggs are normally laid, and in some regions as many as 60. These are the product of more than one female, since the male usually commands a harem of three to five wives at any one time. He nevertheless undertakes most of the incubation himself, and his sheer size and strength are presumably enough to intimidate most predators intent on robbing so desirable a clutch. Most other ground nesters aim to avoid discovery by relying heavily on camouflage. This is the strategy adopted by san

ABOVE A breeding colony
of hole-nesting Carmine
Bee-eaters (Merops
nubicus) in a bank of the
Zambesi River.

BELOW Part of a huge,
densely packed breeding
colony of Gannets (Sula
bassana).

plovers, thick-knees, sandgrouse and night-jars, each of which merges effectively into its own particular background as soon as it sits tightly on its nest. Few of these species use any nesting material, probably because to do so would draw undue attention to the exposed eggs.

Other birds have gone underground in order to escape the notice of predators, either digging their own tunnels or else taking over the abandoned burrows of rabbits, marmots, and other rodents. This style of nesting has been adopted by many petrels and shearwaters, puffins, kingfishers, motmots, and todies. Because they provide a relatively sheltered environment and stable temperature for eggs and chicks, burrows are specially favoured nest-sites of high mountain birds, notably in the South American Andes where tunnel-nesting species include a duck, a dove, a falcon, a woodpecker, and many smaller birds, especially ovenbirds and tyrant-flycatchers.

Surprisingly few desert birds use burrows, considering the extremes of heat and cold they experience above ground. The best-known of these is the Burrowing Owl, which inhabits the deserts and dry grasslands of North and South America. These small, but long-legged owls take possession of burrows discarded by prairie dogs, badgers, skunks, and ground squirrels, though they will excavate their own if the soil is sufficiently light and sandy, digging efficiently with their powerful talons. In common with most other burrow nesters, the owl fashions a spherical nest chamber at the end of the tunnel, bare of any lining. Some species, like bee-eaters and Sand Martins (Bank Swallows), are colonial burrow-nesters, using their bills as picks to chip out tunnels in steep river banks.

Diminutive as it is, the Burrowing Owl dwarfs its relative, the five-and-a-half-inch (fourteen-cm) Elf Owl, which has the distinction of being the smallest bird of its kind. It lives in the arid lands of the south-western United States and Mexico, where it breeds in the abandoned

ABOVE A breeding colony of hole-nesting Carmine Bee-eaters (Merops nubicus) in a bank of the Zambesi River.

BELOW Part of a huge, densely packed breeding colony of Gannets (Sula bassana).

ABOVE A pair of Mallee Fowl *(Leipoa ocellata)* at their nesting mound. The cock bird on the left is scuffing with his feet to adjust the depth of compost covering the eggs.

RIGHT Nest boxes provide hole-nesting species with attractive substitutes for natural sites in trees. Here, a Blue Tit *(Parus caeruleus)* feeds one of its young.

nest-holes of Gila Woodpeckers, bored in the pulpy core of the Saguaro cactus. If, however, these are not available, the owl is equally at home in any suitable cavity it can find in an oak or cottonwood tree.

Nesting in tree holes has been widely adopted by many other sorts of birds to give protection from predators. Surprisingly, even certain ducks have forsaken ground-nesting in favour of hollow trees. Probably nowhere is the risk of predation greater than in the tropics where numerous snakes, lizards, monkeys and giant spiders relish eggs, nestlings and full-grown birds alike. As a result, many tropical birds have resorted to hole-nesting, including parrots, rollers, hornbills, toucans, trogons and barbets.

Even in some natural woodlands, and to a far greater extent in most modern 'managed' woods, there are not enough suitable holes, which often leads to intense competition both within and between species. In Europe, woodpeckers, tits, flycatchers, Redstarts and Starlings are among those who require such sites. The woodpecker has the advantage of being able to chisel out his own hole but even this does not guarantee ownership with so many other birds—opportunistic hole nesters like Starlings, Jackdaws and others—poised to dispossess him if they can, for they can make do with a hole anywhere. A simple but dramatic way of demonstrating just how much pressure there is on the natural holes in a wood is to introduce extra sites by providing artificial nest boxes; this quickly allows many birds to take up residence that otherwise would have failed to establish themselves.

Ideally, a bird should select a hole just wide enough for it to squeeze through in comfort, since a wider one can bring trouble from bigger birds and predators, without excluding smaller ones. Holes of the correct size, however, are rare in nature, so some species initially choose a hole with a bigger entrance than they really need, and then reduce it to the right size. The European Nuthatch, *Sitta europaea*, achieves

this by plastering the entrance up with mud which dries to a cement-like consistency.

This practice has been perfected by all hornbills, except the Ground Hornbill, with the prime motive of keeping out marauding predators. Once the female Silvery-cheeked Hornbill is safely inside her tree-hole nest, she begins to plaster up the entrance, using pellets of mud passed to her by the male outside. Gradually the hole is narrowed down to a fine slit, just big enough for the male to slip his mate nourishing morsels of food. Thus imprisoned, the female eventually hatches the eggs and later on, when her young are ready to fledge, chips her way out. The small hornbills of the genus *Tockus* have evolved a further refinement. The *Tockus* females come out when the young are about half or almost fully grown and the young then wall themselves up again.

Although some of the birds so far described have found ingenious locations for their nests, most show only a slight inclination toward nest-building. Many hole-nesters, for example, are content to deposit only a few chips of wood or bark in the nest chamber, or else leave it bare altogether. Not all hole-nesters, however, are so spartan, and the tits, for example, mould a deep cup of moss, lined inside with hair or feathers.

The forerunners of such nests may have been simple, flat or conical platforms, built on the ground, rather like those still made by cranes, divers, geese, gannets and gulls, from grass, seaweed, reeds, and similar vegetable matter. Here, there is no attempt to weave the material into a coherent fabric, and no special inner lining. Unlike passerines—small perching birds—their nests can afford to be rudimentary since they do not need to cater for a helpless brood of nestlings. Instead, the young are born already well insulated with a thick coat of downy feathers and they are capable of leaving the nest earlier than the young of passerines, sometimes within minutes of hatching.

Instead of laying on top of a nest, the Australian Mallee Fowl has evolved the remark-

able habit of entombing its eggs inside a huge mound of sand and leaves. Effectively this acts like a compost heap, the decaying vegetation producing the heat necessary to incubate the eggs. The cock bird takes several months over the preparation of this incubator, first digging a crater to take a bed of eucalyptus leaves, and then piling on sand to a height of about three feet (one metre). When the mound is ready, the female proceeds to lay a large white egg on top of it every few days, sometimes producing as many as 35 in all. As each egg is laid, the cock buries it in the core of the mound, and thereafter assumes total responsibility for keeping the clutch at a constant 33°C. By scraping away the topsoil and probing with his heat-sensitive tongue in the vicinity of the nest chamber, he can gauge the temperature with extraordinary accuracy, detecting changes of less than one degree. If the test shows that the chamber is getting too hot or too cold, he sets about correcting it by either scuffing off topsoil to ventilate the eggs, or piling more on. Few birds show such devotion to duty; every day for the eight months it takes for all the eggs to hatch, he tends to the mound with almost obsessional enthusiasm. When the chicks do eventually hatch, however, they get no help whatsoever from either parent, tunnelling their own way out and immediately running off into the bush, where they fend entirely for themselves. Compared with most birds, they are exceptionally well developed at hatching, and are able to fly within a week of emerging from the mound.

A number of water and marsh birds have forsaken solid ground for nesting, and instead construct floating rafts. Some, like the grebes, moor platforms of reeds and other aquatic plants to growing stems, so that ideally they can rise and fall with changing water levels and avoid being swamped; sometimes they are too firmly fixed to their substrata and get flooded or left high and dry when the water level changes. Few birds are more at home in these surroundings than the aptly named Lilytrotter or Jacana, which builds a flimsy nest of rushes among lily pads. The bird's weight is so evenly distributed by its immensely long, tapering toes that it can run buoyantly across the water surface, using floating plants as stepping stones. The young are quick to emulate their parents' skill, leaving the nest soon after hatching to scamper off across the lilies.

By far the greatest diversity of nesting skill, however, is found amongst birds which have taken to breeding in the branches of trees. The Fairy Tern regularly lays its single egg in the

The flimsy nest of the Lesser Jacana or Lilytrotter *(Microparra capensis)* which is specially adapted for living on floating vegetation.

merest depression on a branch, or else in the fork of a tree. Apparently oblivious to the hazards involved, it makes no attempt at building a nest, and egg losses are high. While changing positions during incubation, however, the birds seem to appreciate the precariousness of their position, edging towards or away from the egg with extreme care. The chick hatches suitably equipped with powerful claws to stay anchored to its lofty site. If dislodged it instinctively displays a vice-like grip so strong that it can even hang upside down and still right itself.

Few other tree-nesting birds are as casual as the Fairy Tern, and most at least fashion a rough platform of sticks and twigs to house their eggs. Among herons, storks and birds of prey, such nests often grow to enormous proportions, especially if they are used again in successive years by the same pair. Mostly, they are ungainly erections, appearing to rely more on sheer mass than skill to hold them in place.

By contrast, the nests built by most small

passerines in trees and bushes are shapely structures, designed on sound architectural principles to provide the strength and insulation needed to see the vulnerable nestlings safely through to fledging. The task of building, which usually falls to the female, often demands careful selection of particular materials, and great agility and skill to manipulate them into place. The smallest of all is made by the tiny Rufous Hummingbird, which moulds an amalgam of moss, lichens, and spiders' webs into an immaculate bowl, with an internal diameter of just one inch (two and a half cm).

These same materials are favoured by the Long-tailed Tit, which builds a perfectly oval, domed nest with a small side entrance, lining it inside with as many as 2000 feathers. Enclosed nests are also made by magpies, wrens and some warblers, and are especially widespread in the tropics, where the constant battle against predation has also led to a wide range of subtle modifications. South American spinetails first build a huge and impenetrable hollow

ball of thorny twigs, and then attach a long and winding tunnel entrance just wide enough to admit the parent birds.

Other species try to protect themselves by suspending purse-shaped nests from the tip of a branch. The Tailor Bird gains natural camouflage by using the growing leaves; using her slender pointed bill as a needle, and plant fibre as yarn, the female nimbly stitches together the edges of one or more large, hanging leaves, to fashion a funnel-shaped pouch. In this she builds a soft nest cup of fine grass, wool and a few feathers.

The sturdy, globular nests of the Village Weaver, found dotted amongst the branches of trees throughout tropical Africa, are woven throughout with strips of palm leaf. The bird leaves a small entrance hole near the top, nestling under a makeshift porch. The massive communal nests of Social Weavers, looking like some terrible growth threatening to engulf the tree, are an interesting example of cooperative nest-building, sometimes involving hundreds

ABOVE LEFT A Fairy Tern (Gygis alba) sits on its egg, precariously laid in the 'nest', a natural frame of branches.

LEFT The massive nest of sticks built by the Grey Heron (Ardea cinerea) which breeds colonially in tree tops.

FAR LEFT The exquisite domed nest of the Long-tailed Tit (Aegithalos caudatus), moulded from lichen, moss and spiders' webs, and placed for safety in a thorn bush.

ABOVE A Garden Warbler (Sylvia borin) feeds its clamouring young which instinctively beg by straining upwards and displaying their brightly coloured gapes.

of individuals. All the birds first join in laying a thatched roof of coarse straw, before proceeding to weave their separate nests below. The result is hopelessly conspicuous, so Social Weavers often take protective measures by choosing to cohabit with a bird of prey, these unlikely allies living quite peaceably in the same tree.

Not all birds use exclusively vegetable matter for nest-building. Some have become plasterers, using earth and mud, as in the case of swallows, as raw materials for the walls of their nests. Swifts use saliva to bind their nest material together. Perhaps the most sophisticated of all nests, however, is made by the Rufous Ovenbird which lives in the Argentinian pampas. From a mixture of mud strengthened with plant fibres and animal hair, the bird builds a spherical dome with a side entrance leading into a small antechamber, from which a corridor curves away to the grass-lined nest chamber. With this sophisticated arrangement of two sections, the nest is completely protected from

ABOVE The nest mass of the Social Weaver (Philetairus socius) is the result of communal effort, sometimes by hundreds of birds.

LEFT One of the most familiar sights in an African village is a tree laden with woven nests of the Village Weaver (Ploceus cucullatus).

RIGHT The Swallow's (Hirundo rustica) nest of dried mud, plastered on to a suitable beam, is a familiar sight in barns.

BELOW A recently
hatched Black-headed
Gull (Larus ridibundus)
chick, typically insulated
with down and able to
see from birth. The nest,
built on the ground, is a
loose weave of grass and
stems.

the elements, whichever direction they may
come from.

The colour of eggs is often associated with
the sort of nest site a bird uses. Birds that have
enclosed nests, whether in burrows, crevices,
hollow trees, or chambers of their own making,
usually lay white eggs. Open-nesting birds are
more prone to discovery by predators, so their
eggs often merge with the background colour,
with buffs, browns and reds predominating,
variously marked with speckles, streaks, and
blotches. Some water birds, like the ducks and
grebes, have retained whitish eggs but cover
them up when they leave the nest, using whatever material is close at hand; grebes drape
reeds and other pieces of vegetation over the
eggs, while ducks use down from the nest lining.

Another characteristic of a given bird species
is the number of eggs it lays in a clutch. Many
seabirds, such as petrels, auks, and some penguins, and also several large birds of prey, lay
only one egg. At the other extreme, gamebirds
commonly lay at least twelve eggs, and the Bob-

white Quail sometimes lays as many as 24 in
one clutch. However this does not always give
an accurate impression of a species' capacity
for egg-laying in any one breeding season, since
it may lay a second clutch after its first brood
has fledged. In general, birds will continue to
make nesting attempts for as long as the food
supply is favourable enough for them to do so.
The Mourning Dove, for example, commonly
lays up to five successive clutches in the course
of its lengthy breeding season.

Most passerines, many ducks, woodpeckers,
and small waders lay one egg a day till the
clutch is complete, though the interval may be
greater, ranging from five to seven days in
certain gannets and hornbills. Incubation
begins once all the eggs are laid, or sometimes
before, the bird sitting tightly and transferring
the body heat necessary for the embryos to
develop. This incubation period varies greatly
in length between species, being shortest (about
ten days) in some of the smaller passerines,
whose young are born in a relatively undevel-

oped state. Some of the largest birds have the longest incubation spans, such as the seven-week vigil of the Wandering Albatross. Its single chick is also one of the slowest developers, taking nine to eleven months to fledge, during which it experiences the extremes of a sub-antarctic winter.

In some species, the pair take turns at incubating, while in others, one member, usually the female, undertakes all the work, sometimes without leaving the nest to feed from start to finish. Lengthy vigils of this kind usually require the bird to store up considerable body reserves in advance of its ordeal. Even so, it may be quite emaciated by the time the eggs finally hatch. The male Emperor Penguin, which steadfastly incubates alone for an epic nine weeks, ends up almost half the weight he was at the start.

The hatching process itself may take several hours or even days from the moment when the chick first pierces the shell with the specially hardened egg tooth at the tip of its bill. For the parents, hatching signals the start of intense activity. If they face a long period of brood care at the nest, their first job is often to carry off tell-tale fragments of eggshell which might otherwise attract predators. If they are species whose young are helpless nestlings, the parents are soon plying back and forth with the food vital to the rapid growth and development of their young. In passerines, the work load imposed on the parents is formidable; the Great Tit, for instance, feeds its young up to 60 times an hour, almost without pause from dawn to dusk.

It is essentially alien to the instinct of birds to give away food automatically, even to their own kith and kin, so the nestlings have to stimulate their parents to feed them. However, if the young do not beg, the parent, eager to feed them, will stimulate them to do so. In passerines the arrival of a parent bird at the nest instinctively sets off a frantic begging display; as soon as the nestlings are born their every motion and gesture is quite un-

ABOVE LEFT The Long-tailed Widow-bird or Whydah *(Euplectes progne)* is so called from the male's nuptial dress.

ABOVE The Great Hornbill *(Buceros bicornis)* is one of the largest birds to use nest holes in trees.

OVERLEAF Mute Swans *(Cygnus olor)* are devoted mothers and will carry their young like this for added protection.

ABOVE A nestling
Cuckoo *(Cuculus canorus)*
dwarfs its foster parent,
a Hedge Sparrow
(Prunella modularis)
which will tend it
slavishly till it fledges.

mistakably directed at their mouths; throwing
their heads back, and gaping widely, they sway
and wriggle to an incessant volley of shrill cries.
This posture exposes the vivid yellow or orange
colour inside the mouth, and on the swollen
flanges round the bill, acting as a particularly
powerful inducement to the parents to proffer
food to the one quickest to beg. In species with
enclosed nests, where there might be difficulty
seeing in the dim light, the nestlings sometimes
have, in addition, reflective spots inside their

mouths, which help both to elicit food and to
ensure that it lands in the right place.

The chicks of many seabirds are fed with
food regurgitated by the adults. Often the
parent is only persuaded to produce a meal by
the chicks pecking expectantly at its bill. In
Herring Gulls, the chicks focus their attention
on a bright red spot on the otherwise yellow
bill of the adult. Simple experiments, using
models with different colour patterns, have
shown conclusively that without this vital

target point, the young of this species are much less persistent in their efforts to solicit food.

Apart from feeding, the parents also have to attend continuously to nest hygiene. When the young have swallowed food, they eject their faeces encased in conveniently tough gelatinous sacs. The parent then seizes these in its bill, and either swallows them on the spot, or carries them away from the nest. Not all birds are so fastidious, however, and kingfishers in particular are noted for allowing excrement and rotting fish remains to accumulate unheeded in their nesting tunnels.

With so much time and effort invested in raising a brood successfully to fledging, parent birds are understandably vigorous in defence of their offspring. Ground-nesting species are particularly vulnerable to predation, and have evolved various ways of coping with emergencies. In gulls, terns, and waders, the young readily make good use of the striking colour match between their mottled down and their surroundings. If danger threatens, the parents raise the alarm by calling frantically to their chicks, which quickly merge into the background, either by scurrying for cover, or freezing on the spot. Young grebes and young Mute Swans are often carried on their parents' backs.

If all else fails, many birds, ranging from plovers to ostriches, endeavour to divert attention away from their young, and on to themselves instead, by feigning injury. These distraction displays are masterful mimes and remarkably realistic; usually the bird droops a wing as if broken, and staggers ahead of the predator till it is lured safely out of the way.

There is one other threat to a viable nesting attempt, however, from which most birds seem unable to protect themselves. Some birds have long since forfeited their role as parents, entrusting their eggs instead to the care of other species. The success of this strategy depends on host birds failing to detect the alien eggs, and treating them with as much respect as they would their own. It would seem that parasitic species have evolved various adaptations of their eggs, egg-laying behaviour and of their young to counteract any opposition there has been, and still is, to their schemes.

The sequence of events is best known for the European Cuckoo, whose main hosts are the Meadow Pipit, Reed Warbler and Hedge Sparrow. The female Cuckoo first seeks out suitable nests of its intended victims, selecting those with clutches just started. Waiting till the resident pair are absent, she seizes the opportunity to remove an egg and substitute one of her own. Often she is too big to fit into the nest, and has to sit on the rim to lay. Cuckoo eggs are therefore fortified with specially thickened shells, to withstand the impact of dropping to the floor of the nest. In most cases, the egg she lays is a convincing forgery, both in colour and size, and the returning hosts usually fail to notice that anything is amiss. In this way, the Cuckoo may successfully farm out around twenty of her own eggs over a few weeks.

The young Cuckoo normally hatches before the host's eggs, and immediately begins to eject them from the nest on its strong back. If the Cuckoo hatches to find itself in the company of other nestlings, these suffer the same fate. In some species of cuckoos, the host's nestlings are not evicted, but nevertheless succumb in the end, unable to compete with the interloper's voracious appetite. The foster parents are unstinting in the devotion they lavish on their sole charge, which in many cases quickly dwarfs them, as it grows to enormous proportions on a diet originally intended for a whole brood.

The development of parasitic behaviour has arisen quite independently in different families of birds, among cuckoos in Europe, Asia, Africa and Australasia, among cowbirds and a duck in the Americas, and honeyguides and the parasitic whydahs (otherwise known as widowbirds) in tropical Africa. The deception by the whydahs' offspring even extends to mimicking the calls, gape markings and plumage of their hosts' nestlings. Parasitic species have therefore gone to extraordinary lengths to allay the suspicions of their hosts, and it underlines the power of evolution that they have succeeded so well in doing so, as well as showing that there has been rejection of unlike eggs and young for this to have taken place.

BELOW A Nuthatch *(Sitta europaea)* attending to hygiene emerges from its nest hole with one of the nestling's faecal sacs.

97

Cage and Aviary Birds

Man's association with birds goes back to the very dawn of civilization. Wherever he has left behind some tangible record of his culture, whether in art, folklore, religious myth, or simply in the discarded remains of everyday life, there is indisputable evidence that birds were among his earliest companions. Real aviculture, however–the practice of keeping birds in cages and aviaries as objects of curiosity and interest–seems to have been well developed only in societies where time and leisure allowed such pursuits. We therefore have to look to the great empires of the past to trace the true origins of aviculture. Early Chinese pottery, sculpture and silk paintings often portray birds as domestic pets, as do the temple carvings of the Incas. The aesthetic appeal of birds was also strong in ancient Egypt, and many songbirds, parrots and doves were apparently prized as household pets.

Throughout the centuries great expeditions abroad in search of trade and new lands to conquer helped to stimulate the interest in

strange and exotic animals. Alexander the Great was an avid bird fancier, and was greatly impressed by his journeys to India. He had many birds sent home from there, notably Peacocks, which received his protection under law, and the Alexandrine Parakeet which bears his name to this day. Later, the Roman armies brought back colourful parrots and Guineafowl from Africa, to adorn the elaborate aviaries built by affluent citizens. The Crusades and the great voyages of exploration of the sixteenth century further helped to stimulate interest in exotic species, and by Victorian times it had become commonplace and fashionable to keep cage birds.

Most birds kept in captivity were seed or grain-eaters (hardbills), because their staple diet was easy to provide. Cage birds that needed insect food or soft plant material (softbills), were usually kept only if they were particularly hardy species, and if they did not require a too specialized diet. Thus the Romans commonly kept Magpies and Ravens which adapt well to man and enjoy a wide diet. Nowadays, however, we have a much better understanding of how birds live in the wild, and can find substitutes for their natural requirements. As a result, an enormous range of different hardbills and softbills can now be kept in captivity. Even so, many of the more specialized softbills only prosper in the hands of experts, and most people still favour the traditional hardbill species.

By far the largest and most celebrated group of hardbills is the parrot family, which includes the parakeets, parrotlets, macaws, lovebirds, and rosellas, among others. Strikingly colourful, raucous, and playful, parrots have long been prized as pets, even in simple tribal cultures, and were much sought after by early travellers like Columbus, who is said to have included a pair of Cuban Amazons in the spoils he brought back to Spain from the New World.

One of the best known cage species is the Grey Parrot, which occurs widely throughout tropical Africa. It was known to the Egyptians,

BELOW LEFT The African Grey Parrot *(Psittacus erithacus)*, renowned for its talking ability, and one of the longest established cage birds.

RIGHT The Alexandrine Parakeet *(Psittacula eupatria)*, so called from its reputation as one of the birds kept by Alexander the Great.

and was almost certainly the first parrot species to be introduced to Europe. Undoubtedly its popularity as a cage bird stems mainly from its great talent for vocal mimicry, for it can imitate human words and phrases with uncanny accuracy. The group of parrots from South America known as the Amazons are also capable of becoming fluent talkers, and the Blue-fronted, Yellow-headed, and Yellow-fronted species are often kept for this purpose.

It is likely that a talking parrot gives as much pleasure to itself as it does to its trainer. Most probably the bird learns that the better a performance it can put on, the more interest and attention it will receive in return, so there is strong incentive to become word perfect. If, however, it should happen to learn a phrase that the owner dislikes, he can usually rectify this by putting an untrained parrot in with the talker. The pair of them will revert naturally to their own language and the mimic's repertoire of human words will gradually disappear.

Parrots and their relatives are mostly gentle and confiding by nature, and soon form a trusting relationship with humans if handled patiently from a very early age. They can survive to a great age if looked after correctly, and some Grey Parrots are reputed to live for 100 years. This is probably an exaggeration, but certainly there are authentic records of parrots living for over 50 years in captivity.

All cage birds require a well-balanced diet to promote a long and vigorous life—proteins for growth, repair and reproduction, carbohydrates and fat for energy, vitamins and minerals for health. These need to be presented in the correct proportions for a given species, and in a form it can readily handle, so we need to know as much as possible about the bird's behaviour in the wild state. This is relatively straightforward for parrots, since almost all of them have a basic diet of seeds and fruits; the Grey Parrot is especially fond of eating the nuts of oil palms.

Experience has shown that in captivity most parrots thrive best on a suitable mixture of sun-flower, canary, or millet seed, ground nuts, and oats, supplemented with fresh, soft fruits, root vegetables and greenstuffs. Sweet foods have to be strictly avoided, since parrots, and indeed most birds in confinement, lead a much less energetic life than their wild counterparts, and can easily become overweight. Letting the bird out of its cage to fly freely around a room, preferably every day, is essential for maintaining fitness and strength.

The cage itself must be made of stout metal bars, since parrots of all kinds have powerful beaks. As in all birds, the beak is a living organ, and the bird can only check its continuous growth by gnawing regularly at something hard. Parrots can keep their beaks trim if they are supplied with a lump of cuttlefish bone, rich in calcium, and a mineral block to nibble and at the same time they can benefit by eating what they scrape off. A stout piece of branch is also good therapy for the beak, and the bark and fibre can be swallowed to provide roughage for digestion. In addition to wood, a constant supply of grit is necessary to ensure that the bird's digestion functions well.

Finally, parrots and most other cage birds need lots of clean water to drink. They also like to bathe in a shallow dish to keep their feathers clean and healthy, though if you do not want to soak the cage, it is often better to spray the bird with warm water, or even in summer to put the cage outdoors in a light shower of rain.

The sort of cage that would comfortably house an African Grey is usually too small for the macaws, largest and most spectacular of all the parrots, measuring up to 40 inches (one metre) from bill to the tip of the long, graduated tail. Macaws are found only in America, in tropical rain forest ranging from Mexico to Paraguay, where they live exclusively on a diet of fruits and nuts, cracking open the hardest shells with their massive bills to get at the nutritious, oil-rich kernels inside. In the wild, they are more often heard than seen, spending most of their time foraging in the tall forest canopy, either in pairs or in large flocks, and

TOP A well known aviary species, the raucous Red and Green Macaw *(Ara chloroptera)* ranges in the wild from eastern Panama down to north Argentina.

ABOVE A native of the Brazilian rain forest, the Hyacinth Macaw *(Anodorhynchus hyacinthinus)* belongs to the group containing the largest and most colourful of all parrots.

ABOVE With its jaunty crest and playful habits, the Sulphur Crested Cockatoo *(Cacatua galerita)* from Australia and New Guinea is a favourite cage bird.

OVERLEAF A captive flock of Budgerigars *(Melopsittacus undulatus)* showing the wide range of colour varieties which has helped to make it the most popular cage bird of all time.

shrieking excitedly as they fly from tree to tree.

Apart from sheer size, their piercing voice makes them less attractive than the African Grey as household pets, and they are better suited to an outdoor aviary. They are hardy birds and adapt well to temperate climates, so much so that it used to be fashionable in well-wooded English estates to have a flock of free-flying macaws in the grounds. The Red and Yellow (Scarlet) Macaw is one of the best known as a cage bird, though the Blue and Yellow Macaw is superior in talking ability. Lacking the bold, almost garish, colours of its relatives, The Hyacinthine Macaw of Brazil has a splend-dour and nobility of its own, bedecked as it is from head to tail in plumage of deep, cobalt blue.

The main home of the parrots and their relatives, other than South America, is Australia where, apart from Budgerigars, probably the most famous are the cockatoos. Unlike macaws they are birds of open woodland, where flocks may be seen alighting on the ground to feed on

seeds, nuts, berries, and even insects. As cage birds, cockatoos have long been held in affection for their playful and lively nature, and they thrive best in a situation that encourages this instinct. Some learn to mimic and talk quite well, but more often, and especially when excited, they content themselves with hideous screeches, flashing up their crest like a colourful fan. Common cage species are the Sulphur Crested Cockatoo and the Roseate Cockatoo, better known in Australia as the Galah.

Compared with the birds described so far, the remainder of the parrot tribe comprises a variety of much smaller birds, which are therefore somewhat easier to look after in captivity. They include probably the most popular cage bird of all, the Budgerigar. Although modern show Budgerigars are an artefact of domestic life, like a cat or a dog, the wild species is well established in its native Australia, being only one of the large and cosmopolitan group known as parakeets. Wild Budgerigars have the colour pattern known to fanciers as light green, and

merge well with their arid grassland habitat after rain, although they are conspicuous in dry periods. Their habitat provides them with their staple diet of seed. They assemble in huge, roving flocks to feed and drink, sometimes descending in spectacular fashion on some isolated pool of water. Unlike their captive relatives, they lead a precarious, opportunist existence; many fall victim to birds of prey, and severe droughts periodically decimate their numbers. Nowadays, however, they are relatively immune from man, who has made it an offence to keep wild Budgerigars in parts of Australia.

The first live Budgerigars were brought to England in 1840 by the celebrated ornithologist, John Gould, and their winning combination of colour, exceptional tameness, simple tastes, and above average vocal mimicry has made them immensely popular. Moreover, they were found to breed freely in captivity, and large colonies were eventually set up, some of which kept up to 100,000 birds in stock. New colour mutations were bound to appear, and by careful selective breeding, a host of varieties was soon produced, ranging from the grass green of the ancestral stock, to yellow, blue, lilac, white, grey and numerous other intermediates. This gave further impetus to the bird's popularity; the public could now choose the colour of their pet to an extent that dog-owners, for instance, might envy.

Given adequate space and facilities, Budgerigars are quite easy to breed in captivity, and no great experience is required. In an aviary (indoor or outdoor) containing a colony of birds, the sexes will pair up and breed freely as they would in nature, provided suitable nest boxes are fitted. If the owner wants to mate a particular pair of birds, he can keep them separate from the rest of the flock till they form an attachment, and this will probably be maintained when they are returned to the colony. In adult Budgerigars of the wild colour in breeding condition, the sexes can be distinguished by the colour and texture of the fleshy cere around the nostrils, which is shiny and dark blue in the males but rough and dark brown in the females.

The aviary should contain the basic requisites outlined earlier for parrots. With a liberal supply of cuttlefish bone and food, the female will find the extra nourishment she needs to lay the usual clutch of around six white eggs, though she may lay considerably more. The nestlings begin to hatch after about eighteen days, and are naked for about twelve days till the feathers begin to grow. At first they are fed jointly by both parents, and are ready to leave the nest box at about four weeks old. By the time the last chick has gone, the female has usually started her second clutch, so the male continues to feed the young alone till they gain full independence about two weeks later. If the normal sequence is allowed to unfold, and the pair go ahead with their second clutch, the complete breeding cycle takes about four months from start to finish.

Other parrots are harder to breed, but like

Budgerigars, they need a site resembling the tree hole most of them use in the wild. A popular substitute is a wooden beer barrel or other cask, lined at the bottom with a layer of sawdust. Compared with Budgerigars, most parrots lay fewer eggs, often only two or three, and may take much longer to hatch and fledge their young. However, a number of notable successes have been achieved through the careful selection of the right pair and the right conditions, and these have often given more insight into the breeding habits of the species than is known from the wild. There may also be practical rewards; thus, in an attempt to re-establish a small, natural colony, a number of privately bred offspring of Hahn's (Noble) Macaw have been introduced to the island of Trinidad, from which the species disappeared some 50 years ago.

Apart from Budgerigars, many other parakeets are kept as cage birds, although they prefer a lot of flying space and do best in aviaries. The Cockatiel, one of the better known Australian species, is a good bird for anyone who wants to progress from keeping Budgerigars to keeping larger parakeets. Other popular kinds include the Australian rosellas, and various of the South American species called conures.

A historically famous cage bird since Roman times is the Ring-necked Parakeet of India, Arabia and Africa, which closely resembles the Alexandrine Parakeet mentioned earlier. However, Africa is better known as the sole source of the popular lovebirds, a group of small, short-tailed parrots which, as their name suggests, flourish when kept in pairs. The Masked or Yellow Collared Lovebird is a native of northeast Tanzania, where it roams the countryside in vast foraging flocks, making themselves unpopular when they periodically ravage the millet crops.

Last among the parrot tribe are the brilliantly coloured lories and lorikeets, which are widespread throughout Papua, Australia, and Polynesia. Unlike other parrots, they are neither seed nor nut eaters, and have therefore dispensed with strong, crushing bills. Instead, they have a tongue specially equipped with a brush-like tip for extracting pollen and nectar from flowers. In Australia, the blossoms of eucalyptus trees are a favourite source of food, especially for the ubiquitous Rainbow Lorikeet. Renowned for their tameness, they regularly descend in their hundreds on public parks to feed from the hands of visitors. Lories and lorikeets are more challenging to keep in cap-

LEFT Before selective breeding highlighted the yellow plumage, the native Canary *(Serinus canaria)* looked more like this, green above and streaked greenish-yellow below.

RIGHT The brilliantly coloured Rainbow Lorikeets *(Trichoglossus haematodus)* from Australia are nectar feeders specializing on the blossoms of eucalyptus trees.

tivity than other parrots because of their specialized diet, and because they also demand more frequent attention to cage hygiene. Although they have no need of the cuttlefish bone or grit essential to seed-eating species, they do need a certain amount of lime, and possibly other minerals, in their food.

The second major group of hardbill (seed-eating) cage birds are the finches (finch here is used in its bird-keepers sense, to include many small birds in no way related to true finches, but, like them, adapted to feed chiefly on seeds), altogether smaller than the parrots, but lacking their beguiling, eccentric habits. Nevertheless, some of the finches are equally colourful and some have superb singing voices, which no parrot has. Finches also have a particularly long tradition of domestication, and were often the forerunners of the distinct cage bird varieties we know today. The most famous of these is the Canary, which can trace its lineage back over 400 years to the sixteenth century, when it was first imported into Europe from the Canary Islands. The Canary, with its beautiful song, quickly established itself as the most popular bird pet of households throughout Europe, only being ousted in recent years by the more versatile and irrepressible Budgerigar.

From the native stock of green Canaries, judicious breeding has produced a wide spectrum of colour varieties, from white and fawn, through the familiar yellow, to red-orange and cinnamon. Body shape and size have also undergone significant changes, wild birds generally being smaller than their domestic relatives. Usually, it is only the cock bird that sings, and most can perform quite well, irrespective of colour and shape. Nevertheless, the quest to perfect a special variety of Canary has often jeopardized vocal ability, with the notable exception of the Roller variety, which has long been bred to excel at singing.

Canaries and other small finches are probably even easier to keep than Budgerigars. They thrive on a simple diet of canary seed and rape, supplemented with occasional weed seeds, greenstuff and fruit. Like parrots, they also need a constant supply of grit, some cuttlefish bone, a mineral block, and water for drinking and bathing.

A pair of Canaries will breed quite happily in a cage no more than three feet (one metre) long. In the classical procedure, a wooden panel is used to separate the male from the female, but around mid-April (in temperate countries) it is replaced by a wire one. This second partition can be removed altogether when the male begins to interest his prospective mate through the wire mesh, by disgorging food to her from his crop. At this stage, laying is imminent, and the female can be helped by enriching her diet with hard-boiled egg yolk. A bowl or basket, suitably lined with felt and other nesting material like dry moss and grass, wool and feathers, makes an ideal nest site for the usual clutch of four or five eggs. Incubation, which takes thirteen days, is all done by the female, but the male assists her in feeding the young, which fledge at about three weeks old, and are

feeding themselves a week or so later. Some people prefer not to use partitions of any sort, and induce breeding quite simply by giving a nest cup to a pair that have shared the same cage for several months. Either method is equally acceptable.

The Bengalese Finch (an estrildid, not a true finch), with a long history of domestication, has also become tolerant of confined spaces and, like the canary, will breed in a relatively small cage. The bird's origins are obscure, but it is thought to have evolved in Japan over 200 years ago from the Sharp-tailed Finch, already long domesticated in China. Unlike Canaries, Bengalese Finches are available in only a limited number of different colour forms, pure white, fawn, chocolate brown, and combinations of fawn or chocolate with white.

The Zebra Finch is one of the latest additions to the true domestic cage birds, and various colour strains have again been produced. It is an Australian member of the widespread family Estrildidae called weaver-finches or better,

grassfinches, and normally lives in the arid grasslands of the interior. In the wild, Zebra Finches are highly sociable, colonial nesters, breeding whenever the otherwise hostile conditions of their parched habitat improve enough for them to do so. In captivity, they have retained the same opportunism, and are always ready to breed if given a healthy diet. The problem then is often to stop them breeding, for they may become exhausted if allowed to have more than two or three broods a year.

Most other finches are hardly, as yet, domesticated, and have not therefore been modified by centuries of selective breeding like those described above. Accordingly they find it harder to adjust to small cages, and do best in aviaries. Closely related to the Zebra Finch in Australia is the most gaudily coloured of all the so-called weaver-finches, the Gouldian Finch. In keeping with its exotic appearance, it is somewhat delicate and especially sensitive to cold, but if kept warm it readily adapts to aviary life. Its popular African relatives, the

ABOVE The Zebra Finch's *(Poephila guttata)* readiness to breed at the slightest opportunity in the wild makes it one of the easiest species to breed in captivity.

ABOVE LEFT A wild flock of Masked (Yellow Collared) Lovebirds *(Agapornis personata)*, more endearing to bird fanciers than to African farmers who often consider it a pest.

LEFT The Gouldian Finch *Chloebia gouldiae* is named after the famous English naturalist.

ABOVE The male Red Bishop (*Euplectes orix*) on the right is one of the most brightly coloured African weavers. Like many species with polygamous males, the female is drab by comparison.

RIGHT The Java Sparrow (*Padda oryzivora*) belongs to the group of weaver-finches known as mannikins. Originally confined to Java, Sumatra and Bali, it has spread to much of Asia through escapes from captivity.

diminutive waxbills, are much more often kept. They are mostly not only hardy, but are spritely birds and in size they range from the tiny Golden-breasted Waxbill to larger species like the Common or St Helena Waxbill, four and a half inches (eleven cm) long. Last among the weaver-finches, there are the mannikins, which include one of the best-known cage birds, the Java Sparrow. It is a strikingly piebald, robust bird with a heavy bill, and fits in best with birds of the same size which it cannot harass.

The largely African group of weavers, which includes the queleas, bishops and whydahs, which are often kept in aviaries, differ much in appearance and habits from the so-called weaver-finches and are classed separately from them. One of the most exotic looking species is the Red (or Orange) Bishop, in which the male's nuptial plumage consists of glossy black and scarlet set off by a thick scarlet ruff around the head. After moulting in captivity the red parts of the plumage are fiery orange, and orange-yellow if the bird is too closely confined. He is

polygamous in the wild, and therefore welcomes the company of several females in captivity.

Apart from the small finches, several other hardbill species make good aviary birds. These include the handsomely coloured cardinals from America, especially the Virginian (or Red), Red-crested, and Green species. These three are quite large birds, a little smaller than a Song Thrush, and are apt to be aggressive to smaller species, although the Green Cardinal is more tolerant, and can safely be housed with other birds outside its breeding season. Many birds will live quite peaceably with quails, which lead an unobtrusive life running about at ground level, safely out of the way of perching species. A strong favourite is the exquisite Chinese Painted Quail, a mere four and a half inches (eleven cm) long. Some species of small pigeons also make good aviary companions, especially the Diamond Dove.

Larger pigeons give infinitely more pleasure if, instead of being confined to an aviary, they

ABOVE The Common or St Helena Waxbill (Estrilda astrild) thrives in an aviary.

BELOW The Red-crested Cardinal (Paroaria coronata) is not always tolerant of smaller species in captivity.

are trained to accept a roosting place and then allowed to fly freely in the open. The ornamental pheasants, like Reeve's, Silver, Golden, and Lady Amherst's, are even more strictly for outdoors, and can be given the freedom of a large, enclosed garden, though the wings ought to be clipped in certain situations.

As we saw earlier, the other major group of cage birds, called softbills, are more difficult to look after than hardbills. Some, however, take quite a wide variety of food, and amongst these are a number of highly popular household pets. Undoubtedly the most familiar are the Greater and Lesser Hill Mynahs, both of which become quite fearless of man, and have a remarkable aptitude for mimicking voices and other sounds.

For those who prefer their bird to sing, some of the commoner softbills are exceptionally

gifted songsters and are often compared favourably with nightingales. Best known are the bulbuls, Pekin Robin, and the Shama, a chat-like thrush of Indian and Indonesian extraction, and credited with the finest singing voice of all foreign birds. The Shama is also a good mimic, however, and is best isolated from distracting background noises, or it will copy these slavishly and adulterate its natural song.

The South American tanagers are valued less for their voice than their bright colours. Once acclimatized, they are reasonably hardy birds and not difficult to feed, though they do need a varied diet. There are numerous other soft-bills which are much more spectacular looking than the tanagers, but they are less adaptable to aviary conditions. In particular, the truly insectivorous species, like the Paradise Fly-catcher, are often reluctant to accept the inanimate foods offered to them in captivity. In this respect, the hummingbirds are perhaps the ultimate challenge, requiring a diet of nectar and tiny insects that is difficult to provide, so

they should really only be in the care of experts.

Whenever any bird is taken into captivity, the owner must accept total responsibility for its health and general welfare. From the outset, then, the bird should be bought from a reputable dealer who can guarantee that it is fit and well. Everything should be carefully researched in advance, from the most suitable cage size for a Canary, to the sorts of birds that will co-exist happily in a large aviary.

As we have seen, some birds take more readily to confinement than others, and a number have been domesticated for so many centuries that they are thoroughly at home with man. It is now illegal for any unauthorized person to catch and cage British and American birds. Many other countries also protect their native species, not least because excessive trapping has brought some to the verge of extinction. Fortunately, there is a growing awareness of the need to exercise worldwide controls on the traffic in cage birds, so that they can continue to thrive in their natural environment.

ABOVE The Barbary Dove, a traditionally popular aviary and free-flying species.

LEFT The train of a cock Lady Amherst's Pheasant (Chrysolophus amherstiae) which inhabits the high mountains of Tibet and south-west China.

113

Birds and Man

It is impossible to define, in simple terms, man's varied relationship with birds, past or present. In primitive societies struggling with an earth-bound existence, they were often revered as sacred animals, endowed with supernatural powers and infinite wisdom. Eskimo legend has it that they were the winged messengers that carried man to this planet, and elsewhere it was common belief that they were ethereal creatures harbouring human souls.

The relationship between man and birds in prehistoric times was a balanced one. Man was merely another predator in the system, living precariously in small, mostly nomadic groups, with hunting methods too crude to cause more than local reductions in the numbers of birds around him. Later, the advent of a more settled, pastoral life fostered a new sort of contact, in which captive birds were brought into the heart of the community to be used as a dependable food supply.

Significantly, the first birds to be kept for this purpose were either seed-eaters, like pigeons and fowl, or grazers, like ducks and geese, and it seems likely that they began as unwelcome plunderers of crops around human settlements. The more they became acclimatized to man in this way, however, the more they laid themselves open to total domestication. There is good evidence that domestic fowl originated in south-east Asia from the ancestral Red Jungle Fowl, which is still found there in the wild wherever pastoral man has left his mark on the landscape. The fowl's earliest association with man has been traced to India, where it was domesticated around 3200 BC; by 1500 BC it was known in China and Egypt, and eventually reached Mediterranean Europe about 1000 years later.

Similarly, wild ducks, geese, and even swans were tamed to provide a ready source of meat, eggs and feathers. In the Old World, the widespread Mallard Duck was the forerunner of all of the common domestic breeds we know today, except for the Muscovy Duck which originated in South America, where it was domesticated before the Spanish conquest. Ducks are a particularly important resource in modern Thailand, where a common sight is an enormous, tightly-knit flock, herded along by trained dogs.

Domesticated species were not only valuable as a source of food, but also sometimes because of their natural abilities. For instance, the potential of the domestic pigeon (descended from the Rock Dove) as a homing messenger was first exploited by the ancient Egyptians, and the idea was also adopted by the Greeks. The Romans used pigeons to send forth the results of chariot races; sometimes they even released swallows for the same purpose, first catching them at the nest and dyeing them in the colours of the winning rider. Much later, in Victorian times, the spread of railways made it possible to transport homing pigeons rapidly to distant release points, and so helped to popularize the sport of pigeon racing.

Other species were used for their natural ability to find and catch food. The art of flying falcons and hawks was practised as long ago as 1200 BC in the East. About 2000 years later, falconry was adopted as the sport of kings in England, and it has recently enjoyed a revival in the western world. Even so, this ancient skill still flourishes most where it first originated, and China, India, Iran and Arabia are its strongholds.

The Chinese, in particular, have always achieved remarkable success in domesticating and training wild birds of all kinds, and to this day, both they and the Japanese use cormorants to catch fish. However, even they cannot teach the birds to deny their natural instincts and not swallow the fish, so a leather collar is fitted around the neck to prevent this happening. In many parts of the world, sea-going fishermen make use of birds in a much more indirect way: they use the cue of feeding flocks to help them locate the best fishing grounds.

Seabirds themselves have long been prized for their flesh, and still are in some places. To fishermen, sailors, and islanders, their dense

RIGHT Pictured in its native habitat, a male wild Red Jungle Fowl *(Gallus gallus)* which gave rise to the domestic chicken.

114

nesting colonies have always provided an un-rivalled source of fresh meat and eggs. In South Australia, between one-half and three-quarters of a million young Short-tailed Shearwaters are still harvested annually, and are sold in the shops as 'muttonbirds'. Nowadays, the entire operation is subject to strict controls, based on a sound knowledge of the birds' capacity for replacing their losses, and, in spite of this harvesting the species continues to flourish.

On the other side of the world, on the remote Scottish island of St Kilda, seabirds were the former inhabitants' major source of food. Every summer, thousands of Puffins, young Fulmars and Gannets were systematically culled to be salted down for the long winter days. In com-parison with the size of the St Kildan com-munity, the breeding colonies were vast, and partly inaccessible, so that again the recurring toll never posed a serious threat to any of the species. The St Kildans, moreover, were well aware of the debt they owed to the birds, and resisted wholesale slaughter.

In the past, mariners who anchored at remote seabird colonies were often much less scrupu-lous, since they seldom had any long-term interest in the birds. From the Arctic to the Antarctic, indiscriminate pillaging of colonies wrought havoc on seabird populations, especi-ally penguins, shearwaters, and auks. Flight-less birds like penguins were especially vulner-able, and their northern counterpart, the Great Auk, was finally hunted to extinction in 1844 when fishermen killed the last two known survivors on Eldey Rock off Iceland.

A particularly bizarre tale of reckless over-exploitation surrounds the Guanay Cormor-ants, Peruvian Boobies, and Brown Pelicans, which breed in enormous numbers on the arid islets off the coast of Chile and Peru. The birds begin by laying their eggs on the bare ground, but gradually acquire a deep, bowl-shaped nest by the accretion of their own droppings. Over the centuries, these guano deposits have built up to form a thick surface crust. The potential of guano as a fertilizer had been known locally since prehistoric times, but the rich beds had scarcely begun to be tapped until about 1840 when harvesting started on a massive scale. One by one, the islets were stripped down to bedrock, while unknown numbers of birds were killed by workmen on the site. Eventu-ally, stern measures had to be taken to save the industry and the bird populations from total collapse, and all the colonies were declared sanctuaries. Today, the guano industry sur-vives with a more modest output, but recently man has threatened the birds yet again by deci-mating their fish stocks.

Guano is also extracted for fertilizer from the limestone caverns in south-east Asia inhabited by Cave Swiftlets, but these birds enjoy greater fame as builders of edible nests, composed of a salivary secretion which is plastered to the cave roof. Collecting these nests is often a hazardous business, requiring the agility and strength to climb a long bamboo pole. Each year 20–30 tons of these nests are exported from Borneo and other Indo-Malaysian islands, to find their

way into bird's nest soup, the so called caviar of the Far East.

Wild birds are valued for a great variety of natural resources. In South America, the cave-dwelling Oilbird is sought after for its liberal stores of body fat, which the Indians render and use for cooking oil and lamp fuel. The frugal St Kildans wasted none of their seabird harvest, using the stomach oil of Fulmars for lighting and medicinal purposes, the stomachs themselves for gourds, and the feathers for bedding. Elsewhere, feathers are highly coveted for their ornamental value and, up to the early part of this century, America ran a lucrative export trade in egret plumes to the fashion centres of Europe, causing widespread devastation of breeding colonies in the process. At the same time, special farms in South Africa raised Ostriches by the thousand for the plume trade, and though the demand has since fallen away, some birds are still reared as a source of leather.

In addition to these direct, material benefits, birds help man tremendously by being efficient predators of insects and parasites that damage his crops and forests. Usually the extent to which birds can improve a situation is hard to judge, but a few well documented cases exist to show that they can sometimes inflict spec-tacular losses on insect pests. Thus, Hairy and Downy Woodpeckers reduced by half the number of Codling Moth caterpillars over-wintering in a Nova Scotian apple orchard, and Yellow-shafted Flickers have been known to take an even higher toll of corn-borer larvae

ABOVE LEFT A breeding colony of Brown Pelicans (*Pelecanus occidentalis*), one of the species which contributes to the lucrative guano deposits of Chile and Peru.

LEFT A large flock of domestic ducks in Thailand, shepherded along by their owners.

ABOVE The Starling (*Sturnus vulgaris*) whose catholic tastes have made it a successful associate of man in towns and countryside alike.

infesting the cornfields of the Mississippi basin.

Many birds, however, are as partial to the farmer's produce as they are to the insect agents that threaten it, and this has led to heated debate over the relative merits of certain species. In Britain, the Rook and Starling have traditionally been regarded at best as dubious allies of the farmer, and at worst, as enemies. A study of Rooks in 1944–5 revealed that they annually ate around 26,500 tons of corn, while one large poultry farmer blamed Starlings for the annual loss of about 1000 tons of animal feed. Usually, however, Rooks and Starlings only inflict serious damage on a very local scale, and it is too easily forgotten that soil insects form the bulk of their diet for much of the year.

Elsewhere, the situation leaves no such room for doubt, and man finds himself in direct conflict with birds. In Africa, hordes of Red-billed Quelea periodically descend on millet and sorghum crops and strip them like locusts, causing great damage, and sometimes even famine. So far, no really effective defence has been found against the birds, which travel in flocks often a million strong, and breed in colonies covering up to four square miles (10.4 sq. km) of thorny scrub.

In South America, the Eared Dove is another major pest of cereal crops, and there again the authorities are engaged in a constant effort to find suitable control measures. In the campaign against Rooks and Woodpigeons, the European farmer's arsenal now includes bird-scaring devices that produce loud bangs or broadcast the birds' own alarm calls, but these, like the traditional scarecrow, are soon recognized as empty threats. In the end, often the only foolproof remedy is to patrol the fields from dawn to dusk, as boys were once employed to do.

To a large extent, rural man has caused his own downfall through the modern practice of sowing monocultures–crops of a single type– over large areas. These frequently prove an irresistible attraction to certain birds which thrive on that particular kind of food. Under such conditions, a species which was formerly held in check can suddenly multiply at an unprecedented rate and reach pest proportions.

This has also happened in towns and cities, which offer birds excellent nesting and roosting facilities, less risk of predation, plentiful food, and a temperature slightly higher than the surrounding countryside. Some birds, like the House Sparrow and Starling, have thus become closely associated with man. Perhaps surpris-

RIGHT The Rook
(Corvus frugilegus) is
regarded with mixed
feelings by the farmer
but may well do more
good than harm.

ABOVE A small flock of Eared Doves *(Zenaidura auriculata)* which, by the thousand, inflict widespread damage on South American grain crops.

BELOW A pair of Stone Curlews *(Burhinus oedicnemus)*, only one of several grassland species currently threatened by the advance of mechanized farming.

RIGHT The Little or Least Tern *(Sterna albifrons)* likes to nest on beaches, which has brought it into direct conflict with man's leisure activities.

ingly, one of the most successful urban opportunists has turned out to be the Herring Gull, which prospers on the wealth of waste food discarded on city dumps.

In most places, however, the Herring Gull continues to resort to the coast for breeding, where its colonies have expanded rapidly in recent years, often at the expense of other nesting species. Seabirds have only a few places where they can breed in relative safety, and as these are progressively monopolized by the gulls, less enterprising species are forced into more accessible coastal sites, where they face fresh competition from man and his leisure activities. The Little (Least) Tern, which likes to nest on shingle beaches, is one such victim of human disturbance, and recently its numbers have declined alarmingly in both Europe and America.

Many other species are being handicapped by the rapid encroachment of man on their natural habitats. The destruction of forests has long since left its mark on European birds, but

the onslaught continues unabated in many other parts of the world, especially in the tropics. In the United States, this has led to the virtual extinction of the beautiful Ivory-billed Woodpecker, which once flourished in the lush riverine forests of the south.

With the growing emphasis on cultivation, steady inroads have been made into natural grasslands and marginal scrub, threatening the once widespread Prairie Chicken in America. In the plains of Asia, Africa and India, the native bustards are likewise under seige, and in England, the Stone Curlew is fast disappearing from its traditional haunts on chalk downland, where the former sheep pastures have largely come under the plough. Reclamation of land by draining marshes similarly threatens many species of wildfowl and waders, though the proliferation of dams, reservoirs, and gravel pits has been an unexpected bonus for them.

Lately, birds have had to contend with the more insidious hazard of pollution of the en-

ABOVE Herring Gulls *(Larus argentatus)* are bold opportunists, invading cities from the coast to prosper on the left-overs of a consumer society.

OVERLEAF Foraging flocks of seabirds can often help fishermen by pinpointing the location of surface shoals.

121

still in use, and partly because migrant species can pick up DDT elsewhere in their range, notably in the tropics.

The plight of birds and other wildlife brought about by man's pollution of the environment has aroused deep concern, which hopefully promises a more enlightened outlook in the future. Already, urgent steps are being taken to ensure the survival of species imminently threatened with extinction. Perhaps the most celebrated of North America's endangered species is the Whooping Crane, whose total world population in 1941 was probably no more than the fifteen individuals found wintering on the Gulf coast of Texas. At that time, no-one knew where they nested, and only an exhaustive ten-year search finally revealed the survivors' only known breeding grounds, in an area of remote forest swamp in Mackenzie, Canada. Between the two extremes of their range, this minimal population had to survive a 2300-mile (3680-km) migration route twice a year. The cranes were quickly accorded the strictest protection throughout their range, and people supported the campaign to save them with almost crusading zeal. Since then, the crane population has risen to a modest 50 individuals, but recent breeding successes in captivity offer the hope that more may yet be returned to the wild.

Captive breeding has been the salvation of the Hawaiian Goose or Néné, whose remarkable recovery from the brink of extinction is one of the outstanding successes of bird con-

vironment by toxic chemicals. DDT, hailed as a revolutionary new insecticide in 1942 when it was first introduced, turned out to be a biological disaster, causing widespread destruction of animals which it was never meant to affect. Hardest hit were predatory birds, whose prey had already accumulated heavy doses of the chemical from their own diet. As a result, many birds either died, or failed to breed properly, often producing eggs with abnormally thin shells which collapsed during incubation.

Also badly affected have been fish-eating birds, like cormorants, pelicans, and Ospreys, whose populations have been decimated in many areas. Peregrine Falcons and Sparrowhawks have also been affected drastically, as has the Bald Eagle in the United States. With the present ban on the use of DDT in America and many European countries, some beleaguered species are gradually recovering, but many others have remained at a low ebb, partly because other equally noxious chemicals are

BELOW The range of many bustard species has contracted greatly through hunting and intensive cultivation of their natural grassland habitat. Shown here is the Black-bellied Bustard *(Lissotis melanogaster)*.

RIGHT A thriving family group of captive bred Hawaiian Geese or Néné *(Branta sandvicensis)*. Returning birds like these to the wild saved the species from the brink of extinction.

servation. The Hawaiian islands have seen more of their native species disappear than any other archipelago in the world. By 1949, the goose population had been reduced to about 35 individuals through loss of habitat, excessive hunting and grazing, and predation by introduced animals like mongoose, rat, wild pig, cat, and dog. Soon after this, a handful of wild pairs were taken into captivity, some by the Hawaiian authorities, the rest by the Wildfowl Trust in England. Here, the birds' breeding output exceeded even the most optimistic expectations, and over 2000 goslings have since been reared. Some of these birds have been reintroduced into Hawaii to bolster the wild population, which now numbers at least 600 protected birds, and seems secure for the foreseeable future.

Index

Acknowledgments

The publishers would like to thank the following individuals and organisations for their kind permission to reproduce the photographs in this book:

A. F. A. Colour Library (R. Craven) 50–1, (E. H. Herbert) 81, 91, (Don McCaskell) 40 above, 46 above, A. F. I. P. (Daniel Lagadec) 92; ARDEA (D. Avon and T. Tilford) 61 above, 108 below, (Hans and Judy Beste) 4–5, (P. Bunge) 100 above, (D. Burgess) 41, (K. W. Fink) 59 below, 63, 93 right, 112 below right, 126 above, (R. Fleming) 57, (John Gooders) 45 below, (Su Gooders) 42–3, (M. E. J. Gore) 120 above left, (C. R. Knights) 120 below, (Trevor Marshall) 34, (P. Steyn) 36, 52 below left, (W. Taylor) 107, (R. Vaughan) 117, (A. Weaving) 16, 86–7, 90 above, (W. Weisser) 18, (J. Wightman) 108 above, (F. Willock) 79 below; Bruce Coleman 60, 110 below, 111 above, (D. Bartlett) 124 below, (D. & J. Bartlett) 59 above, (R. Borland) 40 below, (E. Breeze-Jones) 68, (J. Burton) 22 above right, 24, (Bob & Clara Calhoun) 62, (B. Coates) 23, (F. Erize) 2–3, (S. Gillsater) 72–3, (D. Green) 113, (C. Laubscher) 112 below left, (L. Lee Rue IV) 83 above, (J. Markham) 55, 58 above, 109, (R. K. Murton) 121, (J. Pearson) 45 above, (G. Pizzey) 76, (G. D. Plage) 82 below, (F. Prenzel) 8 above, (H. Reinhard) 89, 110 above, (H. Rivarola) 75, 111 below, (Alan Root) 52 above, (M. F. Soper) 9 above, 13 above, (D. and K. Urry) 17, (J. Van Wormer) 114–5; A. W. Diamond 22 below, 74 above, 88 above; Robert Harding (Sassoon) 6, 116 below; Eric Hosking 15, 35, 48, 49 above, 58 below, 65, 66–7, 71 below, 98, 99, 100 below, 112 above; Jacana Agence de Presse (B. Rebouleau) 122–3, (Castel) 26, (J. L. S. Dubois) 102–3, (Ducrot) 118–9, (J. P. Dupont) 47, (Ermie) 10, 116 above, (Grossa) 30–1, (Pissavini) 32–3, (V. Renaud) 1, 12–13 below, 14, (F. Roux) 11 above, (Suinot) 74 below, (Sundance) 69, (Vici) 78, (A. Visage) 9 below, 53, (Zeisler) 7, 22 above left; Frank Lane 104, 105, (R. Austing) 19, 61 below, 124 above, (N. Duerden) 46 below, 88 below right, (N. Elliott) 94–5, (W. T. Miller) 33 above, (G. J. H. Moon) 70, (L. Robinson) 77, 84, (C. J. Smale) 74 centre; NHPA (A. M. Anderson) 24–5, (Douglass Baglin) 8 below, (F. V. Blackburn) 39, 125, (S. Dalton) 64–5, (B. Hawkes) 30, 71 above, 85, (E. A. Janes) 88 below left, 96, 120 above right, (P. Johnson) 27 below right, 28 above, 83 below, 93 left, (K. B. Newman) 54, 90 below, (P. Scott) 11 below, (P. Wayre) 52 below right; Natural Science Photos 44–5; Pictor 27 above, 79 above; Picture Library 126 below; Picturepoint endpapers; G. R. Roberts 20, 80; Fritz Siedel 21, 36–7; Spectrum 82 above; Tierbilder Okapia 49 below, 97; ZEFA (S. Bardos) 29, (W. H. Muller) 27 below left, 28 below, (Dr. Seeberg) 101.